C000234476

Beat Dyslexia

4

A step-by-step
multi-sensory literacy programme

Elizabeth Franks • Myra Nicholson • Celia Stone

.

The handwriting script used in this publication is available as a stand-alone product. *Handwriting for Windows* is available from www.kber.co.uk and from LDA.

This pack contains:
    Beat Dyslexia Book 4 – Photocopiable resource book
    Audio CD
    32 Reading and Spelling Cards

Additional copies of the audio CD and packs of the Reading and Spelling Cards are available. Please contact our Customer Services Team on 0845 120 4776.

The rights of Liz Franks, Celia Stone and Myra Nicholson to be identified as the authors of this work have been asserted by them in accordance with sections 77 and 78 of the Copyright, Designs and Patents Act 1988.

Beat Dyslexia Book 4
M10791
ISBN-13: 978 1 85503 437 2
© Liz Franks, Celia Stone and Myra Nicholson
Illustrations © Simon Rumble and Garry Davies
Voice: Dan Strauss
All rights reserved
First published by the authors 1993
Second edition published 2008,
Reprinted 2014, 2015, 2016, 2017

Printed in the UK for LDA
2 Gregory Street, Hyde, Cheshire, SK14 4HR
ldalearning.com

Contents

Preface

The new edition of *Beat Dyslexia!* reflects considerable experience in the teaching of dyslexic pupils. This updated series promises to develop literacy skills by combining successful phonological approaches with the very best of conventional, multi-sensory, structured teaching methods.

The *Beat Dyslexia!* books are designed primarily for dyslexic pupils of all ages, but the careful use of visual and aural approaches, in a clearly structured progression, makes them very suitable for any pupil who may be struggling to acquire literacy skills. The series has been designed to take pupils from the earliest stages of letter recognition through to full literacy. On completion of Books 1, 2 and 3, the pupil will have achieved mastery of the elements required for Key Stage 1 of the National Curriculum. Book 4 aims to support pupils to Key Stage 2 and through the early years of secondary school.

Recognising the need to engage the pupil's concentration, the authors have made the activities and exercises both varied and entertaining. The teacher or tutor is enabled to measure attainment by a progressive series of engaging reading passages and spelling tests.

We wish all success and enjoyment to pupils using these books. You will have the reward of making steady progress as you advance from book to book, enhancing your reading and writing skills every step of the way.

Teacher's notes

Introduction

The *Beat Dyslexia!* series of books has been designed to help any child, teenager or adult who is struggling to read, write or spell. The books may be used by parents, teachers or tutors working on a one-to-one basis or with small groups. Books 1 to 3 work on the basics, introducing all the consonants, blends (e.g. pr, pl) and digraphs (two letters representing one sound: ng, th, sh, ch) and the short vowels. High-frequency words, the alphabet, basic punctuation and grammar (the verb, noun and adjective) are all taught using presentations that are clear and also interesting and entertaining. Book 4 deals with long vowels and other spelling patterns and provides literacy support through primary and early secondary-school level.

The main features of the programme include the following:

- A **carefully structured programme** that helps the learner understand the linguistic and phonological structures that underpin literacy. Pupils learn letter–sound relationships, how letters make words, the significance of vowels and consonants, how to recognise rhyme and syllables in words and how to recognise spelling patterns in the English language.

- A **conventional multi-sensory approach** that encourages the pupil to use most senses in order to learn letter–sound relationships. Looking and saying as well as hearing and writing reinforce learning through visual, auditory and kinaesthetic approaches. Wooden or plastic alphabet letters offer the chance to feel the shape of letters and to link this with speaking the sound, hearing the sound, looking at the shape of the letter and creating a neuro-muscular memory of the movement required to write the letter by hand. This approach is based on earlier work by Orton, Gillingham and Stillman and Hickey, who established the principles of multi-sensory teaching for dyslexic pupils.

- A **controlled vocabulary**, which means that in the early stages of the scheme learners are presented with reading passages made up from words which only contain letters and letter combinations they have already learned. There is also a steady introduction to the high-frequency words of the English language.

- The **Reading and Spelling Pack** and the **wooden alphabet** are an integral part of the programme. Their regular use in the earlier books offers reinforcement learning of the basics of sound–letter relationships as well as practice in the sequencing of the alphabet.

- The **CD** provides the auditory input of the programme, with exercises on sound recognition in words, short-term memory training, dictation and listening comprehension.

How to use *Beat Dyslexia!*

Before you begin make sure you have the following equipment:

Set of wooden or plastic alphabet letters (upper case). Paper alphabet letters are provided at the back of the book for sequencing, but wooden letters are needed for multi-sensory teaching.

Sharp pencil (a pencil grip may be helpful)

Lined exercise book

CD player (and CD provided with this book)

Reading/Spelling Pack cards provided with this book

Set of crayons or felt-tip pens

Timer or stop watch

Flash cards for high-frequency words provided with this book

Scissors

Mirror

- *Beat Dyslexia!* has been carefully designed and structured so that learning is cumulative, and also fun. It is therefore essential to follow the order of the pages and the order of the exercises on the pages. Do not skip pages or sections.

- Try to teach on a regular and frequent basis so that there is reinforcement learning of teaching points.

- Encourage your pupil to practise the Reading **and** Spelling Pack as often as possible. This versatile card pack can be used in two ways:
  1 To drill knowledge of individual letter–sound relationships (as described overleaf).
  2 To develop an understanding of how letters can be assembled to make words. The exercises in this book will help you get the idea. You will then be able to combine the cards collected from all the books to give practice in word building that is appropriate to the individual needs of your pupil.

- The listening exercises on the CD are integral to the programme. Teach your pupil to use the track-finding and pause facilities on the CD player before they start them. A beep alerts pupils to pause the CD while completing the written tasks.

- You can work at the pace that suits your pupil. Try to ensure that each teaching point has been successfully learned before progressing to the next. There are spelling tests and reading passages throughout the books, which will help you gauge your pupil's progress. Remember that praise and encouragement are the keys to successful learning. Ensure all goals are achievable and provide the right challenge for the pupil.

- Additional copies of the audio CD and packs of the Reading and Spelling Cards are available. Please contact the LDA Customer Services Team on 0845 120 4776.

A *Beat Dyslexia!* lesson

Many of the lessons in this workbook are designed to introduce and then reinforce a letter or letter pattern. These lessons always follow the same format and most of the instructions are on the worksheet. The notes below will help you follow the methods shown on those pages and other pages.

Introduction

The letter pattern is introduced with a clueword picture and phrase.

Handwriting

Accurate formation of letters should be established from the beginning, so that handwriting is integral to the learning process – kinaesthetic link.

Identification

The letter pattern is underlined or highlighted in a string of words or letters

Listening activity

The pupil may listen to the audio CD or the teacher may read the script on pages x–xiv.

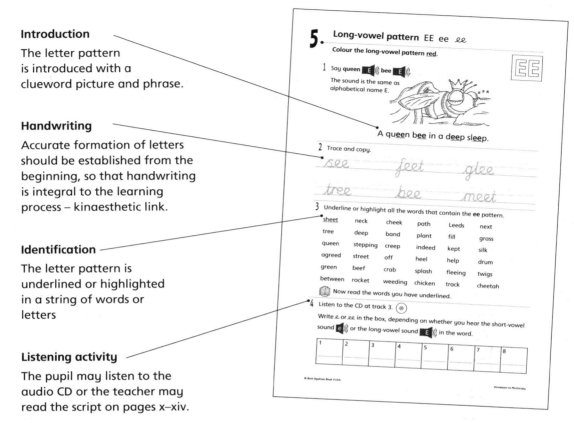

Reinforcement

Further activities reinforce the new letter pattern.

Writing activity

The pupil writes from dictation or creates sentences using the new letter pattern.

Reading

A short passage gives practice in reading the new letter pattern.

Reading and Spelling Cards

This icon means that the pupil should practise using the card sets.

Long-vowel chart

This icon means that the pupil should fill in the long-vowel pattern on the chart on page xix.

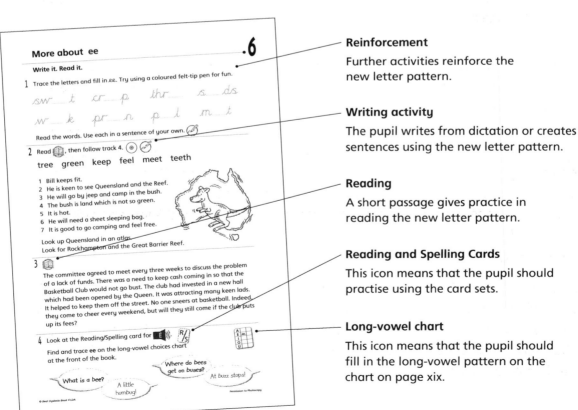

Multi-sensory introduction of the new letter pattern

The pupil says the clueword with the teacher in order to establish the speech sound which goes with the letter pattern. The pupil also traces and copies the handwritten letter form and completes a listening task. The teacher may choose to use the wooden alphabet letters so the pupil can feel the sequence of shapes in a newly introduced letter pattern. The pupil may then spell and read words made from the wooden letters.

Reading and Spelling Pack

The Reading and Spelling Pack is a key component in the *Beat Dyslexia!* programme and should be practised daily. The purpose of the pack is to provide the pupils with practice in looking at and saying letters as well as hearing and writing them.

To practise looking and saying, the pupil should follow this procedure:

1 Look at the letter on the front of the card, and then remember and say the clueword and the sound.

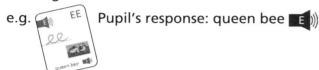

e.g.   Pupil's response: queen bee

2 Turn the card over to check that the word and sound are correct. If the pupil got it right, they place the card on the table, picture side up. If wrong, the card goes to the bottom of the pack, letter side up, so they can have another try.

3 Proceed to the next card.

To practise hearing and writing the pupil should do the following:

1 Listen as the teacher says the letter-sound. The pupil then repeats the sound and adds its alphabetical letter name.

e.g.   E

2 They should then write the letter or letter pattern in their exercise book using joined-up handwriting as taught and using the example on the card to compare with their effort.

The logo reminds the pupil to add the new card to their pack when work on that particular letter-sound has been completed. It is also a reminder to practise the pack, drilling only the letters the pupil has covered so far. This way the pupil acquires confidence in their understanding of the principles underlying literacy skill as knowledge is consolidated in the growing Reading and Spelling Pack.

Handwriting

Use the guidelines provided on the page. You will see that every letter starts on the line. This simple rule is an essential part of learning for the dyslexic or dyspraxic pupil or the pupil with visuo-motor or visuo-perceptual difficulties. In order to achieve the desired result, the teacher must ensure that the pupil always starts on the line, with the entry stroke, and finishes with the exit stroke.

Listening activity

Use this reference section if you are not using the accompanying instruction CD and wish to read the words to your pupil. The exercises are either listening or dictation exercises. Read steadily and clearly. Make sure the pupil uses joined-up handwriting when writing in the box, on the page or in the exercise book.

Page 3 Section 4: DICTATION Listen carefully and write these sentences in your exercise book.

    1 Dad quit his job.

    2 The dog yaps at the vet.

    3 When will Mum mend the zip on this jacket?

    4 The clock stopped at ten to six.

    5 Fill the red jug with milk and pass it to Rod.

    6 The shop is selling fish and chips.   [Track 1]

Page 4 Section 3: Write a tick in the box if you hear a long-vowel sound in the word.

    1 be 2 met 3 so 4 sob 5 pin 6 high 7 up 8 ray 9 rat 10 you.   [Track 2]

Page 5 Section 4: Write *e* or double *ee* in the box, depending on whether you hear the short-vowel sound **e**))) or the long-vowel sound **E**))) in the word.

    1 pet 2 beef 3 green 4 teeth 5 hen 6 tree 7 red 8 sweet   [Track 3]

Page 6 Section 2: DICTATION Listen carefully and write the words and then the sentences in your exercise book.

    1 tree 2 green 3 keep 4 feel 5 meet 6 teeth

    1 Bill keeps fit.

    2 He is keen to see Queensland and the Reef.

    3 He will go by jeep and camp in the bush.

    4 The bush is land which is not so green.

    5 It is hot.

    6 He will need a sheet sleeping bag.

    7 It is good to go camping and feel free.   [Track 4]

Page 9 Section 5: Write *ar* in the box if you hear the **ar**))) sound in the word.

    1 arm 2 bark 3 cane 4 jar 5 burn 6 smart 7 torn 8 apart   [Track 5]

Page 13 Section 4: Write *or* in the box if you hear the **or**))) sound in the word.

    1 form 2 horn 3 Jordan 4 charm 5 bone 6 snort 7 absorb 8 alarm   [Track 6]

Page 14 Section 3: DICTATION Listen carefully and write the words and then the sentences in your exercise book.

    1 north 2 short 3 torch 4 fork

    1 There are sheep to be shorn in the morning.

    2 Gordon's transport is a small Ford car.

    3 Flora can't afford to go to Dorset in March.

    4 According to Lee, Carl is keen on sport.   [Track 7]

Page 15: Listening and following instructions

    1 Draw an arrow pointing north in the circle.

    2 Draw an arrow pointing down towards the base of the triangle.

    3 Draw an arrow pointing east in the square.

    4 Draw an arrow pointing west in the box.

    5 Draw a saucer for each cup in the bottom half of the square.

    6 Draw a star to the right of the moon.

    7 Draw a bird above the circle.

    8 Draw a frame around the picture.

    9 Put a circle in the middle of the star.

   10 Draw a cat sitting on the lowest part of the wall.

   11 Put flames on several of the candles.

   12 Draw a smaller glass to the left of this one.

   13 Put circles round most of the birds.

   14 Draw an arrow pointing from the base of the small cylinder to the top of the large one.

   15 Draw an arrow pointing down from the top of the large tower to the bottom of the small tower.

   16 Put a cross on the widest door.

   17 Put rings around some of the flowers.

   18 Put a flag on the mast and some waves under the boat.

   19 Put a hat on every head.

   20 Put an apple on the lowest tree.

   21 Put a brush on the middle handle.

   22 Copy the pattern of dots and crosses into the blank grid.

   23 Put two candles on the second cake.

   24 Put a cross in the medium-sized box.   [Track 8]

Page 18 Section 3: Minimal pairs. Underline the word you hear.

    1 sheet 2 card 3 fork 4 form 5 sharp 6 shorn 7 creek 8 park

    9 torch 10 feel 11 port 12 green 13 start 14 harp 15 weed   [Track 9]

Page 19 Section 5: DICTATION Listen carefully and write the words and then the sentences in your exercise book.

    1 sky 2 buy 3 shy 4 reply

    1 Parveen will try not to cry.

    2 Why fly to New York?

    3 My feet are not dry.   [Track 10]

Page 20 Section 3: Listen for letter y saying 🔊)) or 🔊)). Tick the correct sound picture in the box.

    1 silly 2 my 3 happy 4 by 5 sticky 6 berry 7 fly 8 pansy   [Track 11]

Page 27 Section 4: Listen and tick the word you hear.

    1 mad 2 fate 3 plane 4 rat 5 van 6 hate 7 back 8 snake   [Track 12]

Page 28 Section 2: DICTATION Listen carefully and write the words and then the sentences in your exercise book.

    1 came 2 brave 3 take 4 make 5 waves 6 safely

    1 Pilgrims came from the North, Scotland and Wales.

    2 They left their haven in Devon and set off in big ships.

    3 They were very brave to take to the waves and make the long Atlantic crossing.

    4 They gave themselves to God.

    5 Many landed safely and began their new lives.

    6 There were plenty of codfish, so they did not starve.

    7 They called their land Cape Cod.   [Track 13]

Page 31 Section 2: DICTATION Listen carefully to each sentence and then write it in your exercise book.

    1 Imran can afford to go to Bradford.

    2 It is windy in the north of Shetland.

    3 Timmy will slip and slide in the slime by the pond.

    4 Is it far to sunny Cornwall?

    5 Lorna will be sixteen on 7th March.   [Track 14]

Page 34 Section 3: DICTATION Listen carefully and then write the words and sentences in your exercise book.

    1 clay 2 delay 3 pray 4 bay 5 pathway 6 Friday

    1 Do not play in subways.

    2 Kay will take her holiday in May.

    3 Can you find Hudson Bay in your atlas?

    4 Sanjay has to study the fishing industry of Norway.

    5 It is a fine day, but Fay has to stay inside and finish her essay.   [Track 15]

Page 38 Section 1: Write _ce_ in the box if you hear the 🔊 sound in the word.

    1 plate 2 place 3 spike 4 spice 5 rice 6 rake 7 race 8 slice   [Track 16]

Page 39 Section 5: Listen carefully and write the word in the correct column on the page.

    1 fence 2 space 3 mess 4 mice 5 boss 6 dance

    7 ice 8 chance 9 less   [Track 17]

Page 44 Section 2: DICTATION Listen carefully to these sentences and then write them in your exercise book.

    1 When are you going to ring him?

    2 Where is the new shop?

    3 Which way shall we go?

    4 Who is going to drive the car?

    5 What is the name of the dentist?

    6 Where has he hidden the cash?

    7 He went in when the bell rang.

    8 Which day is best for you?   [Track 18]

Page 45 Section 4: Write *er*, *or* or *ar* in the box according to the sound which you hear in the word.

    1 stern 2 form 3 marsh 4 lark 5 shorn 6 fern 7 start 8 verb   [Track 19]

Page 50 Section 4: DICTATION Listen carefully and then write the words and the sentences in your exercise book.

    1 wool 2 gloom 3 stood 4 loose 5 bloom 6 roof

    1 Pandas feed on bamboo shoots.

    2 Robin Hood took from the rich and gave to the poor.

    3 The farmer keeps his hen and her brood in a coop.

    4 Mandy has to stoop to pull up the beetroot.   [Track 20]

Page 51 Section 2: Listen carefully and write the word you hear in the family box on the page.

    1 wine 2 took 3 pay 4 mark 5 spark 6 say 7 book 8 line 9 stay 10 fine
    11 stark 12 shook 13 spine 14 brook 15 way 16 lark 17 hook 18 mine
    19 bark 20 pray   [Track 21]

Page 51 Section 3: Listen and write the word you hear under its rhyming partner on the page.

    1 start 2 fire 3 pine 4 fry 5 free 6 born 7 hilly 8 pray 9 pool
    10 stern 11 bold 12 tanker 13 blame 14 look 15 fence 16 price   [Track 22]

Page 53 Section 3: Write *ge* in the box when you hear the 🔊 sound or write *g* when you hear the 🔊 sound at the end of the word.

    1 age 2 stag 3 huge 4 big 5 wage 6 leg 7 rage 8 sage   [Track 23]

Page 54 Section 3: DICTATION Listen to the words and sentences and write them in your exercise book.

    1 edge 2 bridge 3 fridge 4 hedge 5 judge 6 badge

    1 He ran to the edge of the lake.

    2 They bought fudge from the sweet shop on the corner.

    3 He smudged his work when he dropped his pen.   [Track 24]

Page 56 Section 2: Listen to the words and word endings and write them in the correct column on the page.

    1 page 2 judge 3 large 4 twinge 5 wage 6 fridge
    7 charge 8 change 9 stage 10 badge 11 barge 12 range   [Track 25]

Page 60 Section 1: Listen carefully and tick the word you hear.

    1 note 2 rod 3 cope 4 mop 5 hop 6 pope 7 rot 8 code   [Track 26]

Page 67 Section 4: Tick the word you hear.

    1 hug 2 dune 3 puke 4 fuss 5 use 6 duck 7 mull 8 cute   [Track 27]

Page 68 Section 1: Write on the page and fill in the missing consonants to make words.

    1 cute 2 rude 3 tube 4 fluke 5 prune 6 crude
    7 tune 8 use 9 mule 10 nude 11 brute 12 costume   [Track 28]

Page 68 Section 2: DICTATION Listen to the words and sentences and write them in your exercise book.

    1 rule 2 pollute 3 fuse 4 include

    1 Jute is used for making mats, sacking, twine and rope.

    2 The capsule is the nose cone of a rocket.

    3 A flute is a woodwind instrument made from wood or metal.

    4 Fumes from cars pollute the city.

    5 Luke will salute the duke.   [Track 29]

Page 72 Section 2: Listen for the long-vowel sound in each word and write the word in the appropriate column on the page.

    1 bake 2 like 3 use 4 eve 5 bone 6 choke 7 mine 8 duke 9 Pete 10 shake
    11 slime 12 rope 13 theme 14 lane 15 tune 16 mere 17 crime 18 note
    19 cube 20 tape   [Track 30]

Page 73 Section 4: Listen to the words and write *a* in the box if you hear the [a] sound, or *ai* in the box if you hear the [A] sound in the word.

    1 man 2 main 3 rain 4 van 5 paint 6 plan 7 brain 8 clam   [Track 31]

Page 76 Section 4: Write *ow* in the box if you hear [ow] in the word.

    1 howl 2 aim 3 trowel 4 allow 5 stoke
    6 peep 7 crown 8 town 9 faint 10 now   [Track 32]

Page 79 Section 4: Listen to the words and write *ea* [E] *ai* [A] or *oa* [O] in the box according to the sound you hear in the word.

    1 stream 2 brain 3 soap 4 paint 5 team 6 boast 7 sail 8 leave   [Track 33]

Page 82 Section 2: Listen to each word and write it in the correct column on the page.

    1 time 2 tight 3 try 4 might 5 mile 6 my 7 like 8 right 9 why   [Track 34]

Page 84 Section 2: DICTATION Listen carefully to each sentence and write it in your exercise book.

    1 Can you say the name of the train?

    2 Take that snail away from here.

    3 They chose their boat at the show.

    4 The roads were closed because of the snow.

    5 Pete drinks green tea.

    6 It is easy to get rid of these weeds.

    7 Spike likes to fly high in the sky.

    8 Why don't you try to write a letter to your gran tonight?

    9 Use a tool to mend the fuse.

    10 The students said the rules were confusing.   [Track 35]

Other lessons

Working with letters and words you know

These pages aim to give the pupil a deeper phonological understanding of the structure of words. Exercises develop a greater understanding of the sequence of letters and sounds in a word. The significance of the vowel, an appreciation of rhyme and auditory analysis of the way in which words can be differentiated by just one sound are also emphasised.

Essential spellings

These pages teach spelling of the high-frequency words, with the emphasis on joined-up handwriting as an aid to memory. The focus is on irregular spelling patterns (e.g. 'goes') rather than words which can be synthesised from speech (e.g.'next').

Reading passages

These are provided at regular intervals and comprise short passages and stories that are structured to include the letter patterns that are being taught. The pupil's ability to decode is fostered by the fact that they are only asked to read passages that are made up of letters, words and high-frequency words that they have already learned. Thus self-esteem, willingness and a confident ability to decode are generated. All the passages are photocopiable. For pupils with Scotopic Sensitivity Syndrome photocopying onto coloured paper is often helpful.

Long-vowel choices chart

The long-vowel choices chart provides a systematic way for the pupil to build up a list of the spelling choices for each long-vowel sound. Spelling patterns are recorded according to their position in words. For example, 'ee' can be in the main part of a word, as in 'queen'; or at the end of a word, as in 'bee'. Most helpfully, the long-vowel choices chart indicates the frequency of occurrence of a long-vowel spelling pattern by listing it as 1st try, 2nd try, and so on. This helps the pupil to make a reasonable guess at a long-vowel spelling.

Sorting cards

Not included in this book, but recommended as a helpful method for reading practice at this stage, is the making of a pack of forty cards. Select ten words that are to be reinforced. Write these out four times and make cards. The cards may be used for traditional games such as Snap, Rummy, Pelmanism (Pairs) and Happy Families, or simply for sorting.

Reading games

Family Fours (page 25)

This game is played with a minimum of three players. Cards are placed face down in the middle of the table and players in turn pick up and read a card. The first player picks up a card, reads it and then places it face upwards in front of themselves.

The next player picks up and reads a card, looking to see if there are any cards with the same letter or family pattern in front of any other player. If there are, then that player can claim them. In this way a complete family of four cards is built up and the winner is the player who collects most families.

Blackboard Bingo (page 48)

The teacher writes a list of at least fifteen words on the board or a sheet of paper. Each player chooses five or six words from the list and writes them down. The teacher then reads out from the list on the board, at random. Players cross off words on their own lists as they are read out. The first to cross off all their words shouts 'Bingo'.

Cages and Bridges (pages 57 and 58)

This reading game requires a 0–6 dice and a counter for each player. Cut out the chance cards on page 57 before playing the game. Place the counters by the start sign. Players in turn roll the dice and move their counter the relevant number of spaces. The winner is the player who reaches the final space first. A few challenges in the game target the spelling of numbers, which are printed as figures on the board. Make sure a chance card is picked up and read when the pupil lands on a starred space. ✩

Spelling tests (Sp)

At intervals throughout the book, a logo tells the user to ask the teacher for a spelling test. Read the words carefully and clearly. Be sure to include the words in brackets if there is ambiguity about the spelling.

Page 3 Section 3:

1 said   2 can't   3 there (I am going there on Sunday. There is the car.)   4 made (He made a cake.)
5 little   6 going   7 does   8 make   9 like   10 seen (I have seen that film.)   11 people
12 here (Here we are again. Bring that book here.)   13 have   14 are (We are happy.)
15 saw (I saw him yesterday.)   16 coming   17 before   18 look   19 want   20 time

Page 19 Section 4:

1 fly   2 sky   3 dry   4 spy   5 why   6 by

Page 32 Section 4:

1 pride   2 street   3 park   4 storm   5 cry   6 lady   7 shake   8 time   9 green   10 farming
11 morning   12 half   13 bushes   14 almost   15 armies   16 wives   17 cherry   18 any   19 take
20 thought

Page 45 Section 5:

1 like   2 place (location)   3 what   4 march   5 while   6 pencil   7 charm   8 report   9 my   10 only
11 gone   12 could   13 play   14 mice   15 mother   16 heard (I heard him say that.)   17 stay
18 face   19 goes   20 when

Page 52 Section 3:

1 broom   2 shorter   3 their (meaning belonging – Their dog is cute.)   4 better
5 which (question word – Which one do you want?)   6 took   7 harsh   8 sweetest   9 verb
10 wake   11 always   12 shook   13 port   14 paper   15 keep   16 stern   17 shook   18 together
19 spoon   20 there (I went there last week.)

Page 66 Section 3

1 during   2 hedge   3 first   4 mole   5 knew (knowledge – I knew that fact.)   6 year   7 tune   8 rage
9 being   10 stone   11 huge   12 called   13 jogging   14 packed   15 biggest   16 pressed   17 bridge
18 woke   19 cube   20 stopped

Page 78 Section 2:

1 town   2 snow   3 down   4 blow   5 grow   6 allow   7 follow   8 window   9 shower   10 brown

Page 84 Section 3:

1 below   2 friend   3 compete   4 brain   5 frown   6 slow   7 boat   8 might   9 leave   10 above
11 theme   12 shadow   13 write (I will write a letter to him.)   14 show   15 toast   16 trail
17 right (He is right to tell you to turn right.)   18 near   19 told   20 trainers

Guide to logos used in *Beat Dyslexia 4*

	Sound (includes appropriate letter)
	Add new card to your pack and practise the cards you have collected so far
	Listen to CD
	Read
	Repeat and spell
	Write
	Listen to CD and write. The task will usually be a dictation. You will find the appropriate track on the accompanying CD. Instead you may use the CD transcript in these notes to read to your pupil.
	Fill in the long-vowel pattern you have learned on the long-vowel choices chart.
	Ask your teacher to read the spelling test words.

Crossword solutions

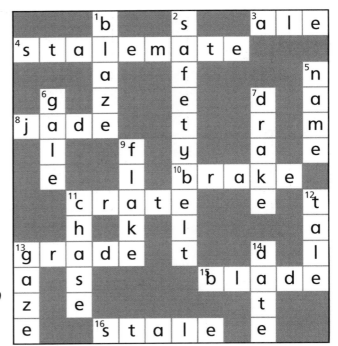

Page 29

Page 55

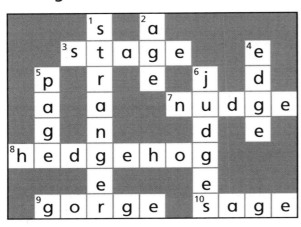

Page 80

Page 74

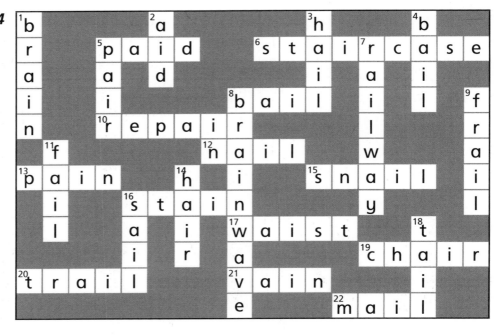

Long-vowel choices chart

Long-vowel sound picture	Open syllable	Main part of word				End of word		
		1st try	2nd try	3rd try	4th try	1st try	2nd try	3rd try
A	a|corn	a-e	ai			ay		
E	e|qual	ee	ea	e-e		ee	ea	e-e
I	i|ron	i-e	igh			y	igh	
O	o|pen	o-e	oa	ow		ow		
U	u|nit	u-e						

1. Are you ready for Book 4?

1 Write the first letter for these words using joined-up handwriting.

_____ _____ _____ _____ _____ _____

_____ _____ _____ _____ _____ _____

_____ _____ _____ _____ _____ _____

_____ _____ _____ _____ _____ _____

2 Write the first two letters for these words in joined-up handwriting.

_____ _____ _____ _____ _____ _____ _____

_____ _____ _____ _____ _____ _____ _____

_____ _____ _____ _____ _____ _____ _____

Are you ready for Book 4?

1 How many letters are there in the alphabet? _____
   The vowels are _____ _____ and sometimes _____.
   The rest of the letters of the alphabet are called _____.

2 Read these short-vowel sounds. ă [a])) ĕ [e])) ĭ [i])) ŏ [o])) ŭ [u]))

   Read these closed-syllable vc and vcc words:

   v c
   had   net   flit   jot   mum   crab   glen

   fox   wet   plum   van   quiz   yes   kin

   v c c
   junk   hand   nest   flint   lost   hump   help

   plank   bring   wasp   with   fish   rich   kiss

3 Read these two-syllable, short-vowel sound words.
   They have vc | cv pattern.

   v c |cv
   pub|lish   kidnap   sunset   inject   absent

   happen   problem   cobweb   husband   index

   petrol   trumpet   public   button   goblin

   wisdom   blanket   mascot   victim   basket

3. Are you ready for Book 4?

1 Write the alphabet in lower-case letters.

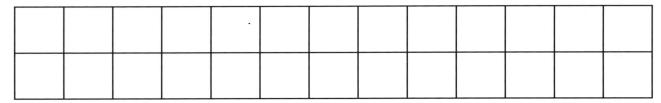

2 Write the alphabet in upper-case letters.

3 (Sp) Ask your teacher for a spelling test.

4 Read these words, then use the CD at track 1 for dictation.

1 Dad quit his job.
2 The dog yaps at the vet.
3 When will Mum mend the zip on this jacket?
4 The clock stopped at ten to six.
5 Fill the red jug with milk and pass it to Rod.
6 The shop is selling fish and chips.

5 Read these high-frequency words.

little   make   look   going   said   away

new   where   down   about   one   house

again   girl   people   many   brother   coming

laugh   tries   because   night   another   were

walk   come   don't   live   does   take

very   here   goes   how   should   now

Getting ready for Book 4

Introducing long-vowel sounds

1   A long-vowel sound says the alphabetical name of the vowel.
    Listen to your teacher saying them and then say them to yourself.

    A   E   I   O   U

2   📖 Read these long-vowel sound, open-syllable words.
    They are called open-syllable words because there is no consonant
    after the long-vowel sound to 'close' the syllable.

    Hī   sō   bē   mē   wē   shē   gō   hē

3   Tick the box when you hear a long-vowel sound. Track 2. ◎

1	2	3	4	5	6	7	8	9	10

4   📖 Read these v｜cv pattern words.

    The first syllable is an open syllable,
    which means that the vowel has its long-vowel sound.

    trī|pod   bā|sin   pī|lot   rō|bot   sī|lent

    tulip   pupil   China   shaken   music

    broken   open   demon   unit   student

    protect   token   chosen   raven   even

    oval   waving   begin   equal   label

5. Long-vowel pattern EE ee *ee*

Colour the long-vowel pattern <u>red</u>.

1 Say **queen** E))) **bee** E))).

The sound is the same as alphabetical name E.

A qu<u>ee</u>n b<u>ee</u> in a d<u>ee</u>p sl<u>ee</u>p.

2 Trace and copy.

see　　　　*feet*　　　*glee*

tree　　　　*bee*　　　*meet*

3 Underline or highlight all the words that contain the **ee** pattern.

<u>sheet</u>	neck	cheek	path	Leeds	next
tree	deep	band	plant	fill	grass
queen	stepping	creep	indeed	kept	silk
agreed	street	off	heel	help	drum
green	beef	crab	splash	fleeing	twigs
between	rocket	weeding	chicken	track	cheetah

 Now read the words you have underlined.

4 Listen to the CD at track 3. (◎)

Write *e* or *ee* in the box, depending on whether you hear the short-vowel sound e))) or the long-vowel sound E))) in the word.

1	2	3	4	5	6	7	8

More about ee

Write it. Read it.

1 Trace the letters and fill in _ee_. Try using a coloured felt-tip pen for fun.

sw__t   cr__p   thr__   s__ds

w__k   pr__n   p__l   m__t

Read the words. Use each in a sentence of your own.

2 Read 📖, then follow track 4. ◎ ✎

tree   green   keep   feel   meet   teeth

1 Bill keeps fit.
2 He is keen to see Queensland and the Reef.
3 He will go by jeep and camp in the bush.
4 The bush is land which is not so green.
5 It is hot.
6 He will need a sheet sleeping bag.
7 It is good to go camping and feel free.

Look up Queensland in an atlas.
Look for Rockhampton and the Great Barrier Reef.

3 📖

The committee agreed to meet every three weeks to discuss the problem
of a lack of funds. There was a need to keep cash coming in so that the
Basketball Club would not go bust. The club had invested in a new hall
which had been opened by the Queen. It was attracting many keen lads.
It helped to keep them off the street. No one sneers at basketball. Indeed,
they come to cheer every weekend, but will they still come if the club puts
up its fees?

4 Look at the Reading/Spelling card for ▪E))). R/S

Find and trace **ee** on the long-vowel choices chart
at the front of the book.

What is a bee?

A little humbug!

Where do bees get on buses?

At buzz stops!

7. Sort the words

1 Read the words and write them using joined-up writing
  under the correct group heading.

squirrel	arm	green	feet	chimpanzee
red	leg	neck	black	piglet
hand	pink	rabbit	chest	sheep

Animal	Body	Colour
e.g. *sheep*	*feet*	*green*

2 Read the words and write them under the correct group heading.

dress	chips	milk	vest	fish
coffee	pants	sweets	socks	beer
jacket	belt	toffee	chops	jam

Clothes	Food	Drink
e.g. *dress*	*chips*	*milk*

Alphabetical order

Syllable counting revision

1 Put out your alphabet letters in an arc shape.

2 Write the letters of the alphabet in lower-case joined-up handwriting.

3 Write the number of syllables in each name in the brackets.

e.g. Nick Ashton (3)   Susan Jennings ( )   Steven Flemming ( )

   Benjamin Peel ( )   Yasmin Crabtree ( )   Judith King ( )

   Sanjeet Patel ( )   Scott Wilson ( )   Emma Munro ( )

   David Buxton ( )   Hassan Yossef ( )   Jonathon Dodds ( )

4 List the names above in alphabetical order, **surname first.**

e.g. 1 *Ashton Nick*   7 _____

   2 _____   8 _____

   3 _____   9 _____

   4 _____   10 _____

   5 _____   11 _____

   6 _____   12 _____

9. Vowel pattern AR ar *ar*

1 Say **star** ar))).

ar (star)   ra   *or*

er   *ar*

er

er   ar

ra

ar   *or*

or

AR

Is M<u>ar</u>s a st<u>ar</u>?   **No! What is it?**

2 Draw a star round every pair of letters which say ar))) above.

3 Trace and copy.

car   *bar*   *star*

harp   *dart*   *arch*

4 📖 👄 Read and spell aloud with your teacher.

car	cart	spark	farm	remark
parking	harmed	sharpen	shark	darling

5 Write *ar* in the box if you hear ar))) in the word. Track 5. ◎

1	2	3	4	5	6	7	8

6 Make words by joining the family patterns inside the stars to the letters outside the stars. Choose the letters for the third star.

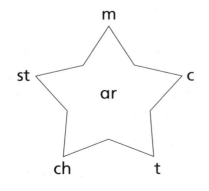

m

st   c

ar

ch   t

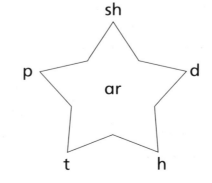

sh

p   d

ar

t   h

ark

More about ar

1 Complete the sentences using the words in the box.

1 _____ has to _____ for _____ at 6 o'clock, so he has set his _____ .	**1)** depart Cardiff alarm Farhad
2 _____ with _____ can _____ you.	**2)** harm Sharks teeth sharp
3 The _____ actress _____ and spilled _____ red punch on the _____ .	**3)** tripped dark carpet charming
4 I went to the _____ to get some fresh _____ for the _____ .	**4)** parsnips market banquet harvest
5 _____ the _____ in the _____ at the back of the _____ .	**5)** farmyard barn Park cart
6 How many _____ does _____ need to fill his star _____ and hit the _____ ?	**6)** target Mark stars chart

2 Underline **ar**. Can you find 13?

Martin parked his car in the car park. He got his diving kit out of the back. He had always been good at swimming and now he had started diving as well. Down in the dark depths he had seen many tropical fish. Once he had seen a shark with very sharp teeth, but it had not harmed him. Not wanting to make himself a target, he had departed smartly.

3

R/S

Why are dogs like trees?

They have barks.

How do you get rid of varnish?

Get rid of r. v _ _ _ _ _

11. Singular to plural

One to more than one

1 At the end of most words, simply add **-s** when you mean more than one.

RULE

e.g. 1 pot (singular)   2 pot**s** (plural)   1 Queen (singular)   3 Queen**s** (plural)

When a word ends in a hissing sound like **-ss -sh -x -ch**, add **-es** when you mean more than one.

RULE

e.g.   1 brush   2 brush**es**   1 glass   2 glass**es**

2 Read the singular form of the word and then trace it, adding **-s** or **-es** to form the plural.

Singular	Plural	Singular	Plural
lunch	*lunch*	wish	*wish*
job	*job*	box	*box*
kiss	*kiss*	seed	*seed*
sock	*sock*	loss	*loss*
fox	*fox*	tax	*tax*
dress	*dress*	dish	*dish*

 Listen for the second beat in these words which end **-es**.

fishes   bunches   boxes   tresses

3 Choose four plural words from Section 2. Write each in a sentence of your own. Write these sentences in your exercise book.

- A sentence is a group of words containing a verb (doing word) in order to make sense.
- Start each sentence with a capital letter.
- Put a full stop at the end of every sentence.
- Put a question mark at the end if you have written a question.
- Use joined-up handwriting.

Essential spellings

12

1 Work across the page. $\longrightarrow$

Read	Trace, naming letters	Write
1 thought	*thought*	
2 being	*being*	
3 almost	*almost*	
4 any	*any*	
5 found	*found*	
6 goes	*goes*	
7 gone	*gone*	
8 heard	*heard*	
9 could	*could*	
10 knew	*knew*	

2 Use mnemonics to help you remember.

<u>o</u>ld <u>u</u>ncles <u>g</u>et <u>h</u>ungry   <u>o</u>ld <u>u</u>ncles <u>l</u>ike <u>d</u>ancing

th<u>ough</u>t   c<u>ould</u>

br<u>ough</u>t   w<u>ould</u>

b<u>ough</u>t   sh<u>ould</u>

© *Beat Dyslexia Book 4* LDA© *Beat Dyslexia Book 4* LDA   Permission to Photocopy

13. Vowel pattern OR or _or_

1 Say **fort** [or]))).

Cadets marching n**or**th to the Roman f**or**t at Y**or**k.

2 Trace and copy.

_or_   _lord_   _sport_
for   _horn_   _scorch_

3

pork north thorn stork morning acorns
orbit platform record transport forget

4 Write _or_ in the box if you hear [or]))) in the word. Track 6. ◎

1	2	3	4	5	6	7	8

5 Trace the letters and fill in **or**.

_t__ch_   _b__n_   _f__k_   _h__n_
_sh__t_   _s__t_   _t__n_   _sp__t_

Use each word in a sentence of your own.

1 📖 Put a ring round the one which doesn't rhyme.
Write the family pattern of the rhyming words. ✏️
Use joined-up handwriting.

e.g. (storm)   shorn   thorn   born   *orn*

sheet   street   sleep   discreet   _____

bar   scar   star   snort   _____

fort   snort   pork   short   _____

barn   corn   worn   torn   _____

been   seen   screen   deer   _____

stork   shark   fork   cork   _____

2 📖

A strong wind is starting up. It is coming from the north. The branches
of the trees are shaking and acorns and beech nuts are dropping off.
The horses are snorting. A small flock of sheep is standing next to the wall.

I think there will be a storm before morning. Then branches might be
torn from trees. It will be dark and wet. The sheep and horses will be in
the barn by then and I shall be snug between the sheets and blankets
on my bed.

3 📖, then follow track 7. ⊙ ✏️

north   short   torch   fork

1   There are sheep to be shorn in the morning.
2   Gordon's transport is a small Ford car.
3   Flora can't afford to go to Dorset in March.
4   According to Lee, Carl is keen on sport.

4

Why did the
man with one hand
cross the street?

To get to the
second-hand shop.

Listening and following instructions

Track 8 ⊚

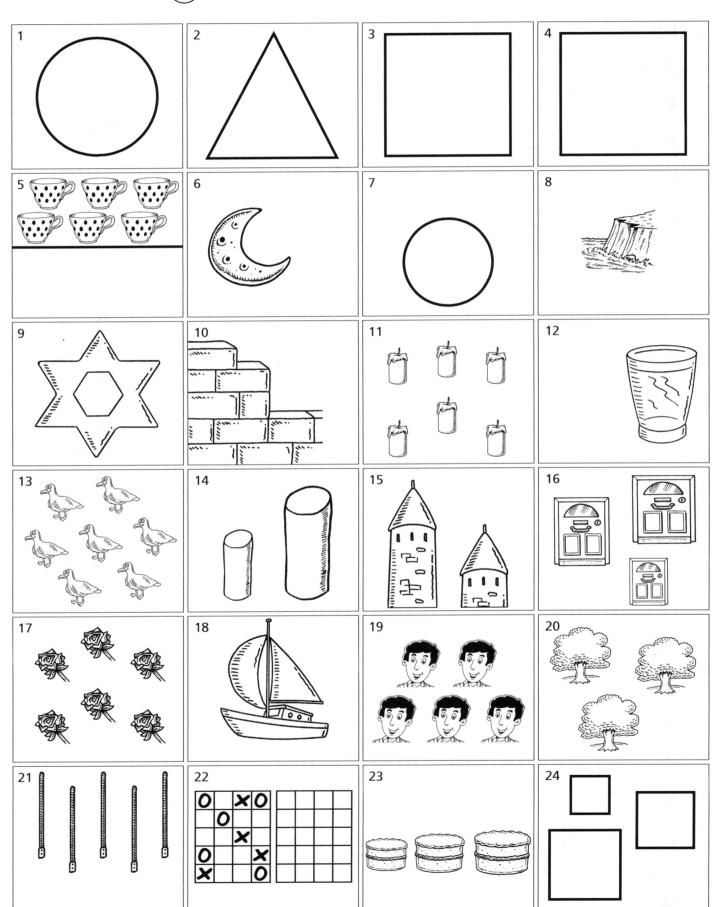

Learn to use your dictionary

You will need your alphabet letters and your dictionary.

1 Put out the alphabet letters in four rows like this.

A B C D

E F G H I J K L M

N O P Q R

S T U V W X Y Z

2   1 Take your dictionary and open it in the middle. You will have divided it in half (½). You will find that you are looking at words which begin with **M** or **N**.

    2 If you now open your dictionary halfway between the beginning and **M**, you will have opened it at the end of the first quarter (¼) and you should find that you are looking at words beginning with **E**.

    3 Now open your dictionary halfway between **M** and the end. You will be about three-quarters (¾) through and you will be looking at words which begin with **S**.

    4 Practise this several times until you can easily find words which begin with **A E M/N** and **S**. You will have learned how to divide the dictionary into **quartiles**:   A–D,   E–M,   N–R,   S–Z.

3 Use your dictionary to see how quickly you can find words which begin with the following letters and write down two words from each section.

	1st word	2nd word
B		
E		
H		
M		
R		
W		

4 Find a telephone directory and look for names that begin with these letters. Write down one for each letter.

M _____   **S** _____

17. Handwriting practice

Trace and copy.

ee

keep   been

Queen   seen

Greek   feed

A queen sleeps between silk sheets.

ar

smart   park

shark   depart

garden   market

Would Charles like to visit Denmark?

or

before   forget

thorn   morning

Portugal is noted for its linen cloth.

1

Read 📖	Use your Reading/Spelling pack to make words	Name the letters 👄	Write ✏️
sheep			
shark			
pork			
park			
short			
keep			

2 Add F, S and M cards to SH, P, K and T.

How many other words can you make using EE, AR, OR?
Write them in your exercise book. ✏️

Can you make ten words?

3 Minimal pairs. Underline the word you hear. Track 9. ◎

1 sheep   sheet   2 card   cart   3 fort   fork

4 form   ford   5 shark   sharp   6 short   shorn

7 creep   creek   8 park   part   9 torn   torch

10 feel   feet   11 pork   port   12 green   greet

13 star   start   14 harp   hard   15 weed   week

19. Letter Y y 𝓎 as a long vowel

Colour the long vowel y <u>red</u>.

1 Say **cry** .

Try not to cry.

2 Trace and copy.

cry   *try*   *dry*

3 📖

fly   dry   fry   pry   try   sly   ply   rely   apply   why

4 (Sp) Put the alphabet letters in four rows as you did on page 16.
Use them to spell the words your teacher gives you.
Remember to replace the letters in the correct row after each word.

5 📖, then follow track 10. (◎) (✎)

sky   buy   shy   reply

1 Parveen will try not to cry.
2 Why fly to New York?
3 My feet are not dry.

6 Find and trace **-y** on the long-vowel choices chart

Why do bees hum?

Because they don't know the words.

Letter Y y 𝓎 as a short vowel

1 Say **baby** 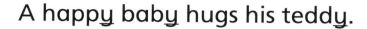.

A happy baby hugs his teddy.

2 📖

hilly   greedy   cheeky   party   carry   lorry   frisky

3 Listen for 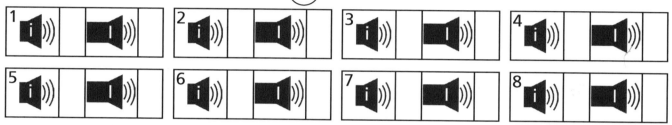 **y** or 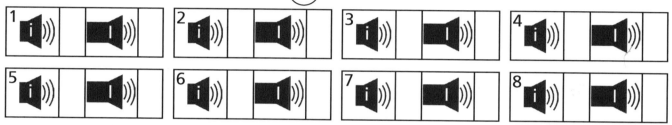 **y** at the end of each word and tick the correct sound picture in the box. Track 11. ◎

| 1 | 2 | 3 | 4 |
| 5 | 6 | 7 | 8 |

4 Make words and write them in your exercise book. ✏

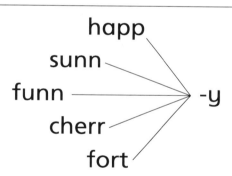

happ
sunn
funn
cherr
fort

-y

Use each of these words in a sentence of your own.

clumsy   hungry   lucky   windy   family   empty

5 📖

The baby is not very happy so she begins to cry. She is called Holly but she is not very jolly. She is unhappy because she needs feeding. Her tummy is empty, which is why she is grumpy. The sly puppy has run off with her dummy. She doesn't think this is funny. She is getting very angry. Billy gives her a teddy to try to distract her, but she only yells more. Oh my! She can't have the dummy because it is filthy. Billy tells her about Humpty Dumpty. He acts silly, puts on a floppy hat and pretends to fall off the wall. He lands with a thud on the carpet. Baby Holly stops crying and starts waving her teddy at Billy.

R/S

21. Making sentences

1   In order to have meaning, a sentence must have a **verb**
(a doing or action word).

Without a verb, a group of words does not make sense. Try reading this.

No verb	Verb
The boy the ball.	The boy **kicks** the ball.

The function of the verb in the sentence is to say what is happening.
Simple sentences have **subject verb object** order like this.

Subject	Verb	Object
The boy	kicks	the ball.

The **subject** is the person (or animal or thing) who (which) is
doing the action.
The **object** is the thing which is having something done to it.

2   Make up **subject verb object** sentences from the words given below.
Write them in your exercise book.

e.g. *Andy needs some sleep.*

Subject	Verb	Object
Andy	drinks	the ball
Daddy	stings	rabbits
Jack	needs	boxes
Flora	fries	the Queen
A wasp	lifts	the lorry
The fork-lift truck	breeds	the garden
Imran	kicks	some sleep
Norman	weeds	coffee
Shireen	wants	the bacon
Mark	parks	some sweets

3   Now **proofread.** This means you should read through what you have
written, checking that you have copied the spelling correctly, used capital
letters where necessary and used a full stop at the end of each sentence.
Finally go back over your work and put a ring round every verb.

Reading limericks

Drawing pictures

1 Draw a picture for each rhyme in the box next to it.

2 Count the number of syllables in each line and write it in the brackets.

e.g. Whenever in need of a feed, (8) The cheetah can run at top speed. (8) It will grab a gazelle, (6) Drag it down for the kill, (6) And be very greedy indeed! (8)	
	When darting about in the park, ( ) Our little dog started to bark ( ) At a man in a car ( ) Who was a pop-star, ( ) So we ran after him for a lark! ( )
There was a sly spy ( ) Whose job was to pry ( ) About plans for a rocket to Pluto. ( ) But when asked, "Could you fly ( ) To that star in the sky?" ( ) His reply was, "Oh no! I can't do so." ( )	
	There was a small lad called Jack Kelly ( ) Who did have a very big belly. ( ) When he went to posh parties ( ) He'd fill up on Smarties ( ) And then finish off with some jelly. ( )
I had torn my shorts on a thorn, ( ) Then was tossed by a bull on its horn. ( ) I feel so worn and torn ( ) That I know in the morn ( ) I shall wish I had never been born. ( )	

23. Long-vowel pattern I–E i–e *i–e*

Colour the long-vowel pattern red.

1 Say **smile** . The sound is the same as alphabetical name **I**.

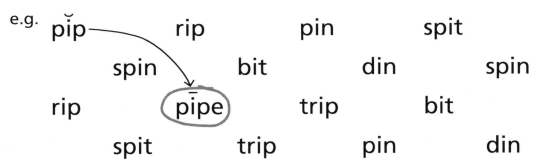

Smile like a crocodile!

2 Link the matching pairs of words. Add **e** to the end of one of the pair.
Put a ring round the **i–e** word you have made and mark the long vowel **Ī**.
Read all the words.

e.g. pĭp — rip   pin   spit

     spin   bit   din   spin

rip   (pīpe)   trip   bit

     spit   trip   pin   din

Q. What is silent **e** doing?   **A.** Silent **e** is making the vowel long.

It turns **i**))) into **I**))).

3 📖 Listen for the final sound in each word.

Fill it in on the sound picture.

e.g. kite [*t*])))   time [ ])))   bike [ ])))   smile [ ])))   ride [ ])))

Did you hear the **e** sound at the end? ☐ Yes ☐ No

4 Finish the puzzles using the letters under each one.

	p	i	n	
	p	i	n	e
s	p	i	n	e

e,s

r	i	p	

e,s,t

r	i	d	

e,s,t

More about i–e

1 Copy in your exercise book twice. Tick the one you like best.

Mike likes to ride his bike.

2 Highlight **-ire**.

fire   wire   tire   desire   squire

spire   retire   inspire   admire   entire

3 Trace, filling in the missing consonants to make words.
Use: n k m r

spi__e   hi__e   wi__e   sli__e   mi__e

fi__e   ti__e   bi__e   li__e   pi__e

4 Choose five words from Section 3 and use them in sentences of your own.
Write the sentences in your exercise book.

5

Mike smiles as he rides his new bike down the hill. He is having the time of his life. He is on a nineteen-mile bike ride. He has a green helmet and he has planned to keep away from cars. At the bottom of the hill he will get onto the canal path. The canal path is free of cars and he will ride along that for about nine miles. Then he will stop for a bite of lunch and a cup of coffee because he will be quite tired and in need of a rest. After lunch he will get going again as he wants to be home by five o'clock.

6

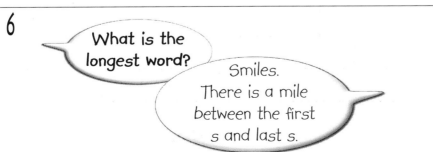

What is the longest word?

Smiles.
There is a mile between the first s and last s.

Looking for letter patterns

Put a ring round each word in the word search.
Write it in the family rhyming box. Cut out each word.
Shuffle. Sort or play Family Fours (see page xv).

ar	*ee een*	*ee eep*	*or*
spark			

g	r	e	e	n	s	p	a	r	k	c	r	y
b	a	b	y	t	h	o	r	n	d	e	e	p
c	r	i	m	e	l	a	d	y	m	a	r	k
q	u	e	e	n	b	o	r	n	t	i	m	e
t	r	y	m	u	m	m	y	s	t	e	e	p
c	h	i	m	e	l	a	r	k	t	o	r	n
b	e	e	n	q	d	i	n	e	s	e	e	n
c	o	r	n	x	k	e	e	p	m	i	n	e
a	r	k	q	f	r	y	z	h	a	p	p	y
w	i	n	e	q	s	p	r	y	f	i	n	e
s	l	i	m	e	x	b	e	e	p	z	p	q

i-e ime	*i-e ine*	*-y* 🔊	*-y* 🔊

The wild duck – reading comprehension

Rex and Ivan went on a trip to the mud banks. To get there, they had to trespass on the local squire's land. They went briskly and silently to try to take a snapshot of a wild duck.

On that cold, dank morning, they hid in the long, reedy marshland grasses. At the moment when the ducks began to fly across the golden morning sky, Ivan held up his camera to the rising sun. Click, click, went the shutter. He got many shots of the ducks flying in a wonderful V formation to their feeding grounds.

As they began to move on, they almost stepped on a duckling with a broken wing. They bent over to pick it up. It felt soft and velvety in their hands. Putting the pathetic object into their basket, they felt a sudden unhappiness come over them. What could they do to help?

They rushed it to the vet, hoping that it could be saved. Luckily the vet's skill meant that the wild duckling was soon back on the mud banks, flapping happily.

Questions   Tick the box which is next to the correct answer.

1 What does trespass mean?   a to overtake ☐
   b to trek ☐
   c to walk over someone else's land ☐

2 What is the rising sun?   a morning sun ☐
   b evening sun ☐
   c setting sun ☐

3 What is the meaning of 'dank'? _____

4 Do you think that the duckling survived? Give a reason for your answer.

_____

_____

5 Ask someone to read to you the poems 'The Mountain Lion' and 'The Snake' by D.H. Lawrence.

27. Long-vowel pattern A–E a–e *a–e*

Colour the long-vowel pattern red.

1 Say **cake** . The sound is the same as alphabetical name **A**.

J<u>a</u>k<u>e</u> b<u>a</u>k<u>e</u>s a squ<u>a</u>r<u>e</u> c<u>a</u>k<u>e</u>.

2 Trace and copy.

Make waves

3

m
sp
f
j
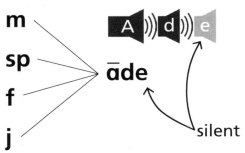
 āde

silent

g
bl
d
l
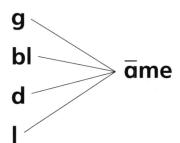
āme

4 Tick the word you hear. Track 12. ◎

1 mad	made		2 fat	fate		3 plane	plan		4 rate	rat	
5 vane	van		6 hate	hat		7 back	bake		8 snake	snack	

5 Name the picture. Write the **a–e** word. ✎

_____ _____ _____ _____ _____ _____

_____ _____ _____ _____ _____ _____

More about a–e

The sound of –are

1

care   bare   dare   fare   hare   mare   rare   stare
spare   snare   glare   ware   beware   compare
prepare   share   square

Choose four of these words to use in sentences of your own to show their meaning. Be careful with **bare**, **fare**, **hare**, **stare** and **ware**. Use a dictionary! Remember to use joined-up handwriting, and don't forget a **capital letter** at the beginning of each sentence and a **full stop** at the end.

2 , then follow track 13.

came   brave   take   make   waves   safely

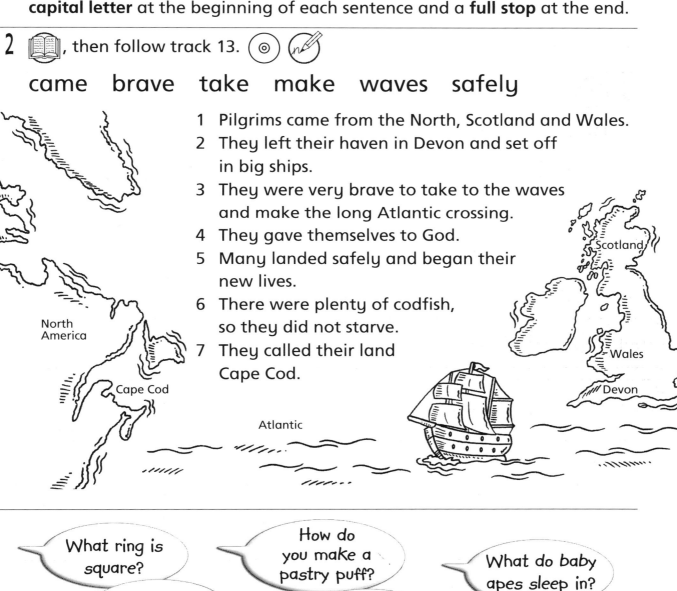

1 Pilgrims came from the North, Scotland and Wales.
2 They left their haven in Devon and set off in big ships.
3 They were very brave to take to the waves and make the long Atlantic crossing.
4 They gave themselves to God.
5 Many landed safely and began their new lives.
6 There were plenty of codfish, so they did not starve.
7 They called their land Cape Cod.

North America

Cape Cod

Atlantic

Scotland

Wales

Devon

What ring is square?

A boxing ring.

How do you make a pastry puff?

Chase it down the lane.

What do baby apes sleep in?

Apricots.

29. Crossword fun – word building

1 tale ale gale jade date brake flake crate chase grade gaze blade name stale drake blaze safety-belt stalemate

Across

3 Beer _ _ _
4 No one can win,
  e.g. the end of a game
  of chess _ _ _ _ _ _ _ _ _
8 Green rock for making
  ornaments _ _ _ _
10 Make a car stop _ _ _ _ _
11 Box for storing or
  transporting things _ _ _ _ _
13 Mark you get in
  an exam _ _ _ _ _
15 Sharp part for cutting
  _ _ _ _ _
16 Old and dry _ _ _ _ _

Down

1 Fire _ _ _ _ _
2 Fitted in a car to keep
  you safe (clunk! click!)
  _ _ _ _ _ _ _ _ _
5 What someone is called by _ _ _ _
6 Very strong wind _ _ _ _
7 Male duck _ _ _ _ _
9 Snow _ _ _ _ _
11 Run after _ _ _ _ _

12 Story _ _ _ _
13 Look at something _ _ _ _
14 12 March 1955 is a _ _ _ _

---

2 Word building. Use these Reading/Spelling pack cards to make words.

Try to write ten different words in your exercise book.

Essential spellings

1 **Work across.** ⟶

Read	Trace, naming letters	Write
1 always	*always*	
2 before	*before*	
3 friend	*friend*	
4 every	*every*	
5 first	*first*	
6 half	*half*	
7 only	*only*	
8 year	*year*	
9 young	*young*	
10 while	*while*	

2 A mnemonic to help you to spell friend.

I to the <u>end</u> will be your fr<u>ien</u>d.

31. Punctuation and using capital letters

1 Put a ring round the words which should **always** begin with a capital letter.

poland   kite   oscar   sky   april   fork   july   nottingham

market   brandy   oxford   bike   hong kong   gareth   madrid

dry   sally   dundee   target   holland   scorch   canada

Did you find 14?

2 Add the punctuation and capital letters to these sentences.

imran can afford to go to bradford
it is windy in the north of shetland
timmy will slip and slide in the slime by the pond
is it far to sunny cornwall
lorna will be sixteen on 7th march

Ask your teacher to check; then follow track 14.

3 Cut out the word strips below and join them to make a meaningful passage. Copy the passage you have made into your exercise book.

How many sentences are there?

happy family. He was thinking

and to spend a short time with her and her

to ride his bike from Dublin to Cork. He was

of asking Sally to marry him.

across to Ireland. He planned

made him smile. He was about to get the ferry

hoping to meet Sally in Cork

morning and the sunshine

Mike was glad to be alive. It was a fine sunny

More plurals

1 The rule for words which end with **-y** is to change **y** to **i** and add **-es**.

RULE

e.g. jell**y** ⟶ jell**ies**   sp**y** ⟶ sp**ies**

The rule for words which end with **-f** is to change **f** to **v** and add **-es**.

RULE

e.g. dwar**f** ⟶ dwar**ves**

2 Write the missing words.

Singular	Plural	Singular	Plural	Singular	Plural
berry		reply			wives
	stories		skies	life	
	lorries	baby			shelves
army		lady		elf	

3 Read the clues on the left and find the matching word in the list on the right. Write the word in the grid.

e.g. red berries	c	h	e	r	r	i	e	s	Smarties
small dog									sky
Mum and Dad and children									holly
rabbits									cherries
insects									pansies
in the garden									puppy
evergreen tree									family
sweets									flies
up above									bunnies

4 (Sp) Ask your teacher for a spelling test.

Listen for every sound. Use joined-up handwriting.
Write the words in your exercise book.

Long-vowel pattern -AY -ay -ay

Colour the long-vowel pattern red.

1 Say **tray** [A])))). The sound is the same as alphabetical
name **A. ay** is found at the end
of a word or syllable.

-AY

"Take the tr**ay** aw**ay**, I s**ay**!"

2 Trace and copy.

ay   *spray*

3 Put out the alphabet quartiles (rows). Pull out the letters **A** and **Y**
and place them together in the spelling pattern **AY**.

B C D

E F G H I J K L M

N O P Q R

S T U V W X Z

AY

<u>A</u>ll

<u>E</u>ggs

<u>N</u>eed

<u>S</u>alt

See how many words you can make by putting letters in front of **AY**.
Make a list of at least six in your exercise book.

4 Trace, adding *ay*, and read the words you make.
Use a coloured felt-tip pen for fun.

pr___   *M___*   *runw___*

cr___on   *p___*   *Frid___*

subw___   *tr___*   *str___*

pathw___   *holid___*   *cr___fish*

More about -ay

1 Compound words. Join the syllables to make two-syllable (beat) words.

e.g. **gate**   mark   *gateway*   grave   worn _____

    hay   day _____   base   mate _____

    pave   stack _____   sub   ment _____

    care   ment _____   grape   way _____

    Sun   free _____   play   vine _____

    trade   **way** _____   care   yard _____

2 📖

Always stay away from stray dogs. A stray dog is one that has run away. It may be lost and hungry. There is not much that you can do. The dog may look as if it wants to play, but it could suddenly turn nasty and repay you with a bite. Do not delay in getting away from such a dog.

3 📖, then follow track 15. 💿 ✏️

clay   delay   pray

bay   pathway   Friday

1   Do not play in subways.
2   Kay will take her holiday in May.
3   Can you find Hudson Bay in your atlas?
4   Sanjay has to study the fishing industry of Norway.
5   It is a fine day, but Fay has to stay inside and finish her essay.

4

What does the Spanish farmer say to his chickens?

"Oh lay!"

What exams do a farmer's children take?

Hay levels.

35. Using the calendar

Finding dates

1   Write the name of the day of the week.

	May					June					July				
Su		7	14	21	28		4	11	18	25		2	9	16	23	30
M	1	8	15	22	29		5	12	19	26		3	10	17	24	31
Tu	2	9	16	23	30		6	13	20	27		4	11	18	25
W	3	10	17	24	31		7	14	21	28		5	12	19	26
Th	4	11	18	25		1	8	15	22	29		6	13	20	27
F	5	12	19	26		2	9	16	23	30		7	14	21	28
Sa	6	13	20	27		3	10	17	24		1	8	15	22	29

e.g.   7 June is   *Wednesday*

2 July is _____

31 May is _____

15 June is _____

30 May is _____

17 July is _____

5 June is _____

21 July is _____

2   Complete the date table.

17/03/72   *17th March 1972*

30/07/02 _____

25/12/92 _____

31/10/35 _____

03/07/00 _____

10/02/99 _____

19/08/44 _____

22/01/06 _____

09/09/77 _____

1

Read	Use your Spelling Pack to make words	Name the letters	Write
life			
late			
my			
safely			
slay			
fly			
mile			
tame			
may			
safety			

2 Write other words you have made in the boxes.

i-e	-ay	a-e

37. Letter patterns cy ci ce – soft c

1 Letter **c** followed by **y, i** or **e** says .

City centre

cycling to the **ci**ty **ce**ntre

2 The letters **y, i** and **e** make **c** say s instead of k.

cy	s	l	cyclops	cycling
cy	s	i	cygnet	fancy
ci	s	i	city	pencil
ce	s	e	cell	cent

3 Put a ring round (ce) (ci) (cy) where **c** is saying s.

lacy	clamp	cellar
decay	decent	exciting
city	central	scraping

4 Write the words from Section 3 under the correct sound.

_____   _____   _____

_____   _____   _____

_____   _____   _____

5 Copy this sentence in your exercise book twice.
Tick the one you like best.

Cindy got a gold pencil in a fancy parcel.

1 Write ce in the box if you hear 🔊)) in the word. Track 16.

1	2	3	4	5	6	7	8

2

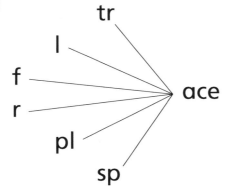

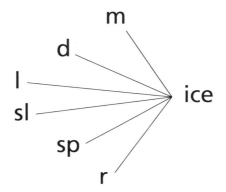

3 Choose two words from each group and write them in sentences of your own in your exercise book.

4 Underline **ce**, **cy** and **ci**. You should find 31.

Grace and Vince decided to cycle to the city centre to go to the cinema. "I thought that film was ace," said Grace. Vince knew a good place to eat, so after the film they went there and had a spicy curry.

On the way back they cycled past the entrance to the palace. It was quite a distance and Vince had to convince Grace that she could do it. They had been out since five o'clock and now it was getting dark.

A policeman stopped them because they had forgotten to put on their lights. "Did you know that cycling in the dark without lights is an offence?" he said.

"We are very sorry, officer," replied Vince.

"Please don't put us in a cell," Grace begged.

"OK then, lights on and off you go," said the officer.

Grace and Vince are good citizens and, anyway, they did not want to have an accident. They put their lights on and cycled back to their place safely.

39. Spelling choices -ss or -ce?

1 In a one-syllable word after a **short** vowel
use -ss, e.g kĭ**ss**.

In a one-syllable word after a **long** vowel
use -ce, e.g. fā**ce**.

2 Mark the vowels long ‾ or short ˘.

ice   space   mice   race   dice

kiss   class   miss   brass   dress

3 Spell the word by tracing and filling in -ss or -ce.

glă___   li___   blĭ___   prĕ___   prī___

plā___   crŏ___   trā___   crĕ___   mĕ___

4 The **s** sound after letter **n** is often spelled **ce**, e.g. da<u>n</u>ce.

da<u>n</u>ce Fra<u>n</u>ce si<u>n</u>ce pri<u>n</u>ce du<u>n</u>ce

cha<u>n</u>ce wi<u>n</u>ce pra<u>n</u>ce tra<u>n</u>ce gla<u>n</u>ce

5 Track 17.

-ce	-ss	-nce

why   buy

happy   very

Try this Cornish pasty. It's yummy.

quite   like

time   shine

He likes to drive to the city to dine.

make   same

came   made

shell   shelf

Take this ball and play.

Tuesday   always

once   race

Grace danced at the palace.

41. Story-writing from pictures

1 Cut out the pictures and their words and arrange them in sequential order.

2 Use the words under each picture to help you create a story about what you see happening. Write the story in your exercise book.

tent   grass   place
camp-fire   lake   hills

Cubs   bus   excited
holiday   yelling   sitting

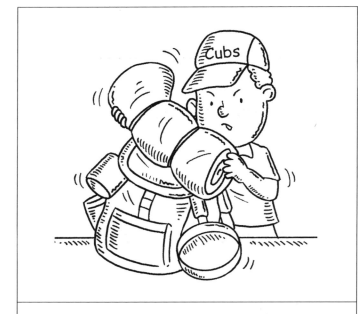

packing   sleeping-bag
rucksack   shorts   socks

sunset   dark   stormy
cold   wet   scared   brave

Crocodiles – reading comprehension

Crocodiles are some of the oldest reptiles. They have existed for 65 million years. They are dragon-like with their long bodies, sharp teeth and strong hides. They lay their eggs and pile them in nests made of rotting plant life.

Their habits are sly. Sometimes they bask in the hot sun on the rocks or hide in the shade of the reeds. At other times, they drift by with just their nostrils poking out of the water, until some unsuspecting victim creeps down to the bank for a drink. Suddenly and swiftly they dart out and with one quick snap the victim is taken. The crocodile then sinks into the deep, dark water, killing its victim by suffocating it. The carcass is kept there in a watery grave until it rots and decays. Crocodiles feed on the carcass when it is well rotted.

Sadly, crocodiles are farmed as well as hunted for their hides, which are used to make handbags and sandals.

Comprehension questions

1 A crocodile is a _____. (fish, rodent, reptile)

2 How do crocodiles protect their eggs?
   Start the sentence with the word 'Crocodiles'.

3 Describe a crocodile.

4 What word is used in the passage to describe the crocodile's habits?

5 Do crocodiles eat their victims alive?

6 Write a few sentences about **one** of the following:

   a How you became a victim of a crocodile. How did you escape?
   b A visit to a theme park, safari park or zoo.
   c Should crocodiles be farmed?

43. Consonant diagraph WH wh *wh*

1 Say **whale** ))). **Wh** is usually found at the beginning of words.

Where does the **wh**ite **wh**ale live? In the Arctic.

2 Do you remember from Book 3 that most question words begin with **wh**?

Answer the questions below.

What is your name? _____

Where do you live? _____

When were you born? _____

Whom do you like? _____

Which school do you go to? _____

Why did the chicken cross the lane? _____

_____

3 Trace and copy.

wh   why   where

4 Fill in *wh*, trace and read. Use a coloured felt-tip pen for fun.

___ack   ___ale   ___ite   ___im

___arf   ___eel   ___at   ___eeze

___y   ___ich   ___ile   ___en

More about wh

Common confusions

1 Fill in the **wh** question word and put a **?** at the end of each question. Remember to start with a capital letter.

_____	have you put the white crayon
_____	way is the quickest
_____	will the bus arrive
_____	is going to sing the solo

2 Choose a word that makes sense. Cross out the wrong word.

1 When/Went are you going to ring him?

2 Where/Were is the new shop?

3 Witch/Which way shall we go?

4 Why/Who is going to drive the car?

5 What/Want is the name of the dentist?

6 Where/Were has he hidden the cash?

7 He went/when in when/went the bell rang.

8 Which/Witch day is best for you?

, then follow track 18.

3 Fill in **went, when, where** or **were**.
Add capital letters and punctuation.

1 _____ is he going to find out _____ she plays tennis

2 _____ the bell rang they all _____ in to lunch

3 _____ they hoping to go to Cornwall for their holiday

4 they _____ trying to find the place _____ they had camped before

5 the police arrived _____ the alarm _____ off

6 we _____ going to ask them _____ the coffee shop was

4

What's white on the outside and green on the inside and hops?

A frog sandwich.

45. Vowel pattern ER er *er*

1 Say **swerve** er))), **bumper** ə))).

Oo, er!

<u>Er</u>! Sw<u>er</u>ve or you'll hit my bump<u>er</u>!

2 Trace and copy.

er   herb   pepper

3 Underline all the words with the **er** pattern. Use your ruler.

Read these words and mark the number of beats (syllables) in the brackets after each word.

e.g. **pap<u>er</u> (2)**   **kerb (1)**   terminal ( )   copper ( )   permit ( )
    fern ( )   her ( )   card ( )   evergreen ( )   start ( )
    better ( )   verb ( )   spark ( )   splutter ( )   deed ( )
    hamster ( )   herd ( )   jerk ( )   report ( )   water ( )

4 Write *er*, *or* or *ar* in the box according to which sound you hear in the word. Track 19. ⊚

1	2	3	4	5	6	7	8

5 Put out your alphabet in the four quartiles (rows).

A–D, E–M, N–R, S–Z

Sp Use the wooden letters for a spelling test.

More about er

1 📖 Fill in *er*.

Ch_____vil is a h_____b we like to put into a dinn_____ or supp_____ dish.
It is not difficult to grow but it likes some shade from hot summ_____ sun.
An odd corn_____ of the garden bord_____ can be set aside for planting
h_____bs such as mint, parsley, basil and rosemary. H_____bs can help
in the garden by attracting the butt_____flies and the hov_____flies.
They can be put on the compost pile to act as f_____tiliz_____.

H_____bs should be gath_____ed before they go to seed. Put them in the
blend_____ and then in the freez_____ as ice blocks. They can then be
popped in the stock pot as needed. Tender h_____bs can even be kept
ov_____ wint_____ in the kitchen or the cons_____vatory.

2 Complete the sentences using the words in the box. ✏️

1 The grass has got _____ and _____. The _____ will have to cut it with a _____.	gardener longer greener strimmer
2 There will be _____ baked in _____ for _____.	butter dinner lobster
3 "Put the _____ in _____ from one to fifty," said the _____.	master order numbers
4 Do not _____ his _____. She has a bad _____.	sister anger temper
5 She had a soft pink _____ and a _____ necklace to go with the ring on her _____.	silver finger jumper

3

What kind of dog goes into a corner every time a bell rings?

A boxer.

What do you get when you cross a killer whale with a helicopter?

A helichopper.

R/S

47. Suffixes -er -est **and comparisons**

The suffixes **-er** and **-est** allow you to compare one thing with another, e.g.:

Yesterday was **wet**, today is **wetter**. Let's hope tomorrow will not be the **wettest** yet.

1 Draw pictures in each box to show you understand these.

small ▢   smaller ▢   the smallest ▢

2 Write the words to complete the table.
Letter **y** at the end of a word changes to **i** before a vowel suffix.

e.g. sweet	sweeter	the sweetest
short		the shortest
	bolder	the boldest
funny	funnier	
	wider	the widest
cuddly		the cuddliest
lazy	lazier	
dry		the driest
	braver	the bravest
merry	merrier	

Notice:

good	better	the best
bad	worse	the worst

3 Complete these sentences .

1 Her dad is _____, my dad is _____, but Wendy's dad is _____.

2 Ted's dog is _____, Gwen's dog is _____, but Kevin's dog is ____.

Do you know these sayings? The more the _____. The bigger the _____.

4 Look in *The Guinness Book of Records*. Find out who was the tallest man.

Jupiter's anger – reading comprehension

Jupiter was the king and master of all the gods. He was also the god of thunder and always carried a thunderbolt in his left hand. Jupiter decided to come down from the sky to see how human beings were living. He was shocked to find that people were so unkind and brutal to one another. His anger was so deep that he decided to wipe out every mortal under the sky and to scatter their belongings to the four winds.

The sky got blacker and then it began to glimmer and shimmer as a number of his forked thunderbolts flickered across the darkness. After the claps of thunder, big drops of rain began to fall. The rivers started to rise and water gushed over the banks and onto the crops of rice. The land got wetter and muddier.

However, one man, who had the gift of seeing into the future, had made an ark for himself. He was clever and quicker than the rest and had constructed his ark with only a hammer and plenty of timber. He filled his ark with his animals, his geese and his ganders, as well as other things he needed. He had to pester his wife to hurry and enter the ark for shelter and safety.

The north wind gusted and water fell from the sky in sheets. Parts of cities were washed away and in some places there was no shelter at all. Animals were swept along on the racing torrent of rushing rivers. The ark was tossed about on the rising water, over trees and small hills. The man and his wife began to shiver together in their berth.

At last Jupiter called an end to the storm and the ark came to rest on top of a big hill. The man and his wife staggered out but, despite their hunger, they sacrificed their ram to Jupiter. Later, they prayed that mankind would be spared. Jupiter listened to their prayer and sent Hermes to tell them "All will be well." For a time, the world was indeed a better place in which to live.

1 Questions
   1 Who was Jupiter and what made him so angry?
   2 What happened when Jupiter sent his thunderbolts from the sky?
   3 What did the wise man put in his ark?
   4 Where did the ark come to rest at the end of the storm?
   5 Describe the view from the ark when it came to rest after the storm.

2 Highlight every **er** pattern you can find. List 15 **er** words in your exercise book. Use these words to play Blackboard Bingo (see page xvi).

49. Vowel pattern OO oo *oo*

Can be short or long. Colour the long-vowel pattern <u>red</u>.

1 Say c**oo**k sp**oo**n .

Who t**oo**k the c**oo**k's sp**oo**n?

---

2 Trace and copy.

oo   cook   spoon

boot   choose

3

boŏk	coŏk	look	took	stood
troōps	foōd	scoop	cool	hoot
shook	hood	crook	wood	good
shoot	stool	stoop	fool	tools

---

4 Name the picture and write the word.

_____   _____   _____   _____

_____   _____   _____   _____

More about oo

1 Put a ring round every word with an **oo** pattern you can find.
You should find 15.

e.g.Kanga(roo)spoonLiverpooldustbinandboomerangbassoondaystooplook
smoothlydoomsbeetrootbedroomstarfishsnookerbaboonballoonhood

2 Read the clue and fill in the missing letters to make the word.

midday		oo	
keep feet dry with them on		oo	
a horse's foot		oo	
in a short time		oo	
bite food with it		oo	
keep exotic animals here		oo	
swim in it		oo	
shines in the dark		oo	

3 Compound words. How many can you make?

broom   land   ball   shine

mush → stick   berry

wood   foot   tooth   stood

moon   under   goose   room   brush

4 , then follow track 20.

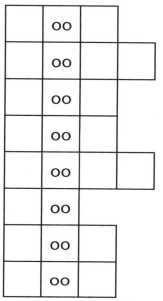

wool gloom stood loose bloom roof

1 Pandas feed on bamboo shoots.
2 Robin Hood took from the rich and gave to the poor.
3 The farmer keeps his hen and her brood in a coop.
4 Mandy has to stoop to pull up the beetroot.

5

What do you call a boomerang that won't come back?

A stick.

51. Word families and rhyming

1 Match the word to its rhyming partner by writing it in the box.
e.g. storm

storm	*form*

haze   spice   jumper   hook   dance   harm
space   stay   roof   stare   plate   winter

bumper	
	skate
gaze	
	mare
hoof	
	farm

rice	
	cook
chance	
	face
way	
	splinter

2 Write the word you hear in the family box. Track 21.

dine	look	bay	dark

3 Listen and write in the word you hear under its rhyming partner.
Track 22.

tree	smart	torn	cry	silly	fine	tray	wire

mice	pence	fern	old	banker	fame	tool	book

There or their?

1   **There** – tells you where, place.
        e.g. He ran here and **there**.
            Who is out **there**?

    Their – shows belonging.
        e.g. They have lost **their** cat.
            Their dog is fat.

2   Complete the sentences by writing *there* or *their*. 🖊

    1   Have you been _____?

    2   _____ they are, skipping across the sands.

    3   I left my bag down _____.

    4   They went to _____ maths lesson.

    5   _____ plan is to get _____ and back
        before ten.

    6   _____ hats are black, but _____ socks
        are red.

    7   They all inspect _____ kit.

    8   _____ is a flock of ducks at the pond.

    9   _____ mum has a bad back.

    10 Some mums and dads make _____ kids
        go to bed before ten o'clock.

3   (Sp) Ask your teacher for a spelling test.
    Listen for every sound.
    Use joined-up handwriting.

53. Letter patterns ge gi and *gy*

1 Letter **g** followed by **e**, **i**, or **y** says **j**))).

A **ge**ntle **gi**ant at the **gy**m.

2 Trace and copy.

ge   cage   wage

stage   gym

3 Write *ge* when you hear **j**))) or *g* when you hear **g**))) at the end of a word. Track 23. ⦿

1	2	3	4	5	6	7	8

4 Fill in *ge* **j**))) at the end of each word and then read the words. Note the long-vowel sound before -ge and -nge.

cā___   ā___   stā___   bar___

hū___   pā___   chān___   rān___

strān___   wā___   lar___   rā___

5 Choose six words and write each in a sentence of your own in your exercise book. ✎

1 Say **bridge** .

Will **Ge**or**ge** bun**ge**e jump off the bri**dge**?

2 Trace and copy.

hedge   *lodge*

3 , then follow track 24.

ĕdge   brĭdge

frĭdge   hĕdge

jŭdge   bădge

1 He ran to the ĕdge of the lake.
2 They bought fŭdge from the sweet shop on the corner.
3 He smŭdged his work when he dropped his pen.

4 Underline all the -dge words.

e.g. Sometimes brĭ**dge**s have rĭ**dge**s or lĕ**dge**s.

1 You may see badgers at the edge of the wood.
2 Do not nudge her or she is likely to smudge her work
and that will make poor Bridget mad.
3 Madge ransacked the fridge, looking for fudge.

Now mark all the vowels in the **-dge** words short ˘.

55. More about -ge and -dge

1 Underline or highlight **Ge ge** saying **j** , and read.

George and Gemma clambered excitedly into the Range Rover, looking forward to a happy day at Grange Safari Park. It was the largest of its kind in Wales. Gemma wanted to try out all the latest rides in the fun park. Her friends reported that the Terror Gorge was the most exciting of all.

George, who was interested in wildlife, looked forward to a lazy trip on a large, white, swan-shaped barge. He could drift by on the fringe of the gardens with their cages full of screeching parrots and other exotic species. Mum and Dad were not looking forward to being in charge of the jackets, the picnic, and the funding of refreshments such as sandwiches, drinks, ices and sweets.

2 Crossword

Across
3 Where you see drama.
7 Push gently.
8 An animal with prickles.
9 Eat too much food.
10 Wise person or herb.

Down
1 You don't know him.
2 How old you are is your ___.
4 He fell over the ___ of the cliff.
5 Part of a book.
6 People who decide on legal matters.

3

What do jelly babies put on their feet?

Gumboots

R/S

Letter patterns gi ge gy **and** -dge

1 📖 **ge**, **gi** and **gy**, and say 🔊 **j**.

gem   giant   gender   ginger   Egypt   engine

gypsy   gentle   Germany   agent   suggest   legend

danger   orange   giraffe   gym   passenger   magic

---

2 Track 25. ◎ ✏️

long vowel + *ge*	short vowel + *dge*	long + short vowel + *nge*	ar + ge + *arge*

---

3 Trace, filling in 🔊 **j** *ge, gi, gy, dge* or *j*.

1 _____*or*_____ made apple _____*elly* and blackcurrant _____*am*.

2 The _____*ntle* _____*raffe* _____*umped* over the ____*n*___*r* cat.

3 The _____*u*_____ said he was a *dan*_____*r* to the public.

4 The *passen*_____*rs* on the _____*umbo*_____*et* were flying to *E*_____*pt*.

4

What goes ninety-nine plonk?

A centipede with a wooden leg.

R/S

57. Chance cards for Cages and Bridges game

See page xvi for instructions.

Hurry up! Track likely to subside. Go forward 4 places.	**Sorry, no luck!** Boot lace snapped. Go back 1 square while you replace it.	**Hooray!** Wind behind you speeds progress. Go forward 5 squares.	Bitten by a snake. Stay very still until the ambulance responds to your 999 call. Miss a go.
Care needed here as pathway is obstructed. Jump 2 places.	Helicopter finds you and flies you on 20 squares.	Bad storm forces you to shelter in the cave. Miss a go.	Chased by wild cave-dwelling monster. Hurry on 9 places.
Slide down the bank for a refreshing drink. Miss a go.	This is a lucky magic card. Keep it in case you need to escape from a cage.	Charmed by the landscape, you decide to rest and relax. Miss a turn.	A stray mule carries you on your way. Go forward 8 squares.
Bitten by a tarantula. Go back 11 places to pick up an antidote.	Stop to dig for hidden gold and gemstones. Miss 2 goes.	Good fortune shines on you. This is a magic card. Use it to unlock the next cage.	Running out of food. Stop to do some fishing. Miss a go.

Cages and Bridges game

.58

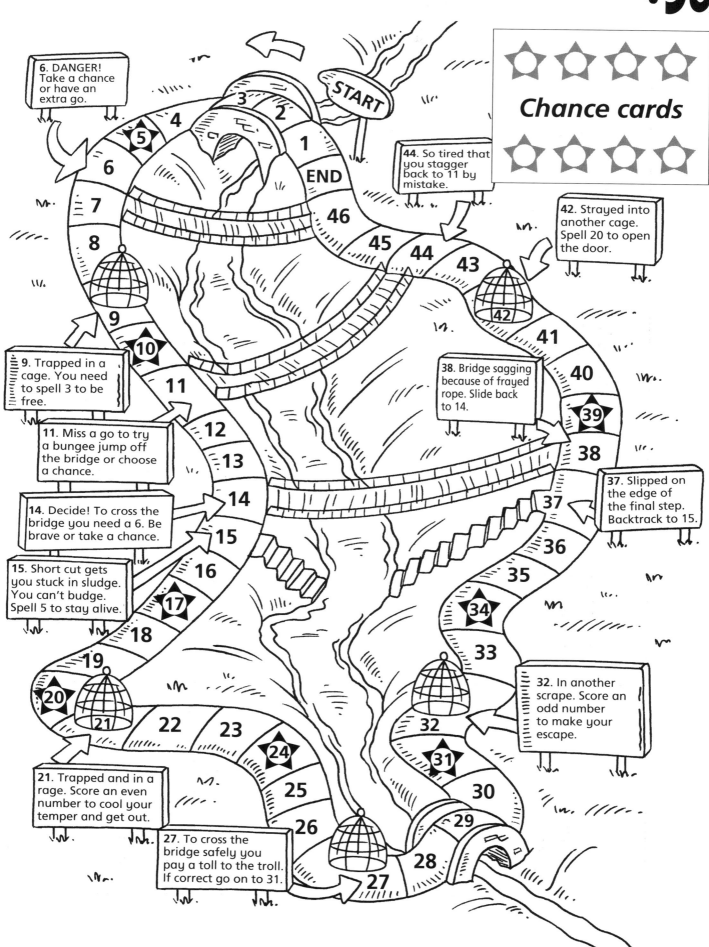

Chance cards

6. DANGER! Take a chance or have an extra go.

44. So tired that you stagger back to 11 by mistake.

42. Strayed into another cage. Spell 20 to open the door.

9. Trapped in a cage. You need to spell 3 to be free.

11. Miss a go to try a bungee jump off the bridge or choose a chance.

14. Decide! To cross the bridge you need a 6. Be brave or take a chance.

15. Short cut gets you stuck in sludge. You can't budge. Spell 5 to stay alive.

38. Bridge sagging because of frayed rope. Slide back to 14.

37. Slipped on the edge of the final step. Backtrack to 15.

32. In another scrape. Score an odd number to make your escape.

21. Trapped and in a rage. Score an even number to cool your temper and get out.

27. To cross the bridge safely you pay a toll to the troll. If correct go on to 31.

59. Long-vowel pattern O–E o–e o-e

Colour the long-vowel pattern <u>red</u>.

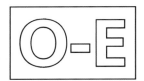

1 Say **nose** . The sound is the same as alphabetical name **O**.

Cl<u>ose</u> your lips and open your n<u>ose</u>. Don't sn<u>ore</u>!

2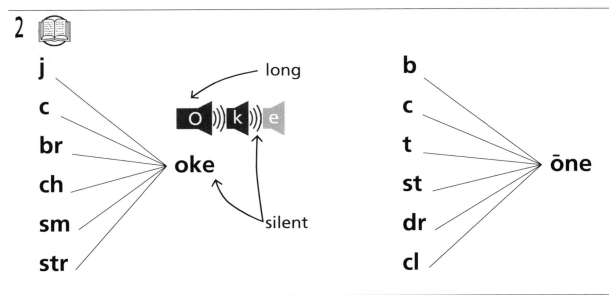

j
c
br   **oke**
ch
sm
str

b
c
t
st   **ōne**
dr
cl

3 Trace and copy twice in your exercise book. Tick the one you like best.

Go home and get some rope.

4 Name the picture. Write the **o–e** word.

_____ _____ _____ _____ _____

_____ _____ _____ _____ _____

More about o–e

1 Tick the word you hear. Track 26.

¹ not		note		² rode		rod		³ cop		cope		⁴ mope		mop	
⁵ hope		hop		⁶ pop		pope		⁷ rote		rot		⁸ code		cod	

2 Trace, filling in the missing consonants to make words.

Use: p k s

spo__e   ho__e   ro__e   bro__e

slo__e   jo__e   co__e   no__e

3 Choose four words from Section 2 and use them in sentences of your own.

Write the sentences in your exercise book.

4

more   tore   sore   shore   wore   score

restore   before   implore   explore   bore   store

5

Dave had been keen to explore the shore, but as he tore down the grassy
slope towards the waves, he did not know what was in store for him.
He wore his old sandals and his feet were sore. Perhaps this was why he
tripped on a stone. When he didn't get up, Rose thought it was a joke.
Then with a note of panic, Dave spoke. "I think I've broken a bone.
I hope Mum's at home. Ask her to come quickly. I don't think I can
cope without her."

6

How do you keep a skunk from smelling?

Hold his nose.

61. Voles – reading passage

1

Voles are closely related to rats but, unlike rats, their noses are a blunt shape, not sharp. They are mammals and exist in most parts of England. They came from the Continent after the end of the Ice Age.

The large water vole lives on the banks of canals, rivers and lakes, and in marshes. It likes to dive into the water and submerge itself, whereas the rat prefers to swim on the top.

Voles feed on grass, plant shoots and seeds. Nests are made under grass tufts or fallen trees, or in holes on the banks of rivers. Breeding is from March to September, when litters of three to six babies are born. Water voles can be seen sitting on stones, nibbling food or washing their faces.

2 Put a ring round the odd one out.
Then write the family letter pattern in joined-up handwriting.

e.g. 1 slope	(mop)	rope	cope	_ope_
2 pin	wine	pine	dine	
3 shape	cape	map	drape	
4 creep	step	steep	deep	
5 fork	dark	spark	lark	
6 cherry	berry	merry	dry	
7 rice	price	space	spice	
8 bridge	wage	fridge	ridge	
9 root	shoot	hoot	hot	
10 spray	pray	pry	pay	

Common confusions

Study the examples carefully and then fill in the blanks with the appropriate words.

1 want or what

e.g. **What** would you like for lunch? We **want** fish and chips.

1 _____ do you _____ to do when you arrive there?

2 I _____ to see _____ he will do next.

3 I _____ to wander on the common to watch the kite-flying competition. _____ do you _____ to do?

4 Is that _____ you _____ to watch on TV?

2 to, two or too

e.g. **To** eat **two** eggs at one meal is **too** much.

1 It is _____ much _____ expect only _____ people to carry that crate.

2 I think you are _____ late _____ see the film. There's only room for _____ more inside.

3 He is twenty-_____ and therefore _____ old to run in this race.

4 It is _____ bad that she couldn't go _____ see her _____ old friends.

3 where and were

e.g. **Where** are my boots? They **were** in the hall this morning.

1 _____ did you put those seeds you _____ going to plant?

2 _____ _____ you last week?

3 _____ you at the shop _____ the fire broke out?

4 _____ have you been and what _____ you doing?

4 when and went

e.g. **When** the party ended they all **went** home.

1 The police arrived _____ the alarm _____ off.

2 _____ the bell rang they all _____ out to play.

3 He _____ for a long walk by the river _____ the sun went down.

4 She _____ to Italy _____ she retired.

63. Long-vowel pattern EA ea *ea*

Colour the long-vowel pattern <u>red</u>.

EA

1 Say **cream** E))) **tea** E))) .

The sound is the same as alphabetical name **E**.

Cr**ea**m t**ea**s, pl**ea**se.

2 Trace and copy this sentence in your exercise book. 🖊

Each peach is a treat.

3 📖

beach	heal	teak	steam	dream	least
tea	deal	pea	peach	meals	bean
treat	beast	leak	tear	team	seal
heap	veal	heat	feast	jeans	meat (beef/pork)

4 How many **ea** words can you find?

The words go across as well as down.

b	e	a	c	h	w	v
e	a	t	h	e	a	l
a	z	t	e	a	k	f
s	t	e	a	m	y	e
t	e	a	p	e	s	a
q	a	m	e	a	l	s
t	r	e	a	t	x	t

Did you find 14 words?

1 Underline or highlight **ea**.

Would you like to hear about the funny dream I had last night? My dear friend Jean and I were going to swim in the sea. To get there, we had to leap over a stream. I cleared it easily but Jean could not leap the stream. The reason for this was that her legs were too weak and she could not reach the far bank. She fell in the stream and I was fearful that she would disappear under the water. I was pleased to see her face appear and I grabbed her by the ears. When Jean had recovered from this ordeal we ran across the beach and into the clear clean sea. After our swim we had a picnic meal sitting on the beach. It was a real feast of sandwiches with lean meat, and cream cakes as an extra treat. I was just about to eat my cake when I could hear my name being said over and over. It was Mum calling for me to wake up. "You could at least have let me eat my cream cake," I screamed unreasonably.

2 Read the clue and fill in the missing letter or letters to make the word.

_____ the floor with a mop and bucket. | | | e | a | |

A small river like a brook. | | | e | a | |

Polite word to use to ask for something. | | | e | a | |

Not playing by the rules of the game. | | | e | a | | | |

Rich fatty content of milk. | | e | a | |

Fantasies when asleep. | | e | a | |

Fish swim in this salty water. | e | a | |

Some rodents communicate this way. | | | e | a | |

To take goods without payment. | | | e | a | |

3

65. Handwriting practice

which   when

while   what

together   brother

never   paper

number   water

door   floor

change   arrange

Look, somebody took that large balloon.

whole   home

come   some

He woke, chose clothes to put on, and has gone.

teach   please   each

I dream about a beach by the sea.

other   better

Look again at the doubling rule and past tense -ed

1 Remember to double the final consonant of a **vc** word before a vowel suffix.

e.g.
vc	vowel suffix		vc|cv
win	+ ing	=	win|ning

Do not double if the base word has **vcc** structure or if the suffix begins with a consonant.

e.g.
vcc	vowel suffix		vc|c v
help	+ er	=	hel|per

vc	consonant suffix		vc|c v
wit	+ ness	=	wit|ness

Try these and use **vc\|cv** patterning to check your answer.

grip	+ ing	=		mud	+ y	=
pack	+ ing	=		slim	+ er	=
pop	+ ing	=		jump	+ ing	=
rest	+ less	=		hot	+ est	=
slip	+ er	=		swift	+ er	=
stop	+ ing	=		fast	+ est	=

2 Remember **-ed** for the past tense ending.
The spelling is not always the way it sounds.

e.g.
jumpt	✗	jumped	✓
stopt	✗	stopped	✓
yelld	✗	yelled	✓

kick	+ ed	=		dress	+ ed	=
bump	+ ed	=		shop	+ ed	=
call	+ ed	=		push	+ ed	=

3 (Sp) Ask your teacher for a spelling test.
Write the words in your exercise book.
Use joined-up handwriting.

67. Long-vowel pattern U–E u–e *u-e*

Colour the long-vowel pattern red.

1 Say tube . The sound is the same as alphabetical name **U**.

A h**uge** t**ube** of c**ube**s.

2 Trace and write in your exercise book. ✏

A huge hug helps.

3 📖

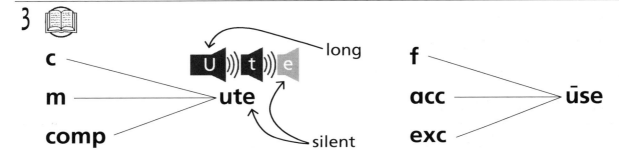

4 Tick the word you hear. Track 27. ◎

¹hug		huge		²dune		dun		³puck		puke		⁴fuss		fuse	
⁵use		us		⁶duck		duke		⁷mule		mull		⁸cute		cut	

5 Link the matching pairs of words. Add **e** to the end of one of each pair. Put a ring round the **u–e** word you have made and mark the long vowel ū.

📖

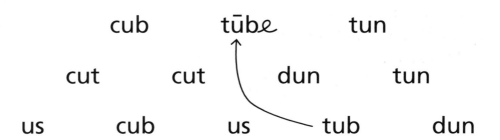

cub   tūbe   tun

cut   cut   dun   tun

us   cub   us   tub   dun

More about u–e

1 Fill in the consonants to make words. Track 28.

1 _ u _ e   2 _ u _ e   3 _ u _ e

4 _ u _ e   5 _ u _ e   6 _ u _ e

7 _ u _ e   8 u _ e   9 _ u _ e

10 _ u _ e   11 _ u _ e   12 _ u _ e

2 📖, then follow track 29. ◎ ✏

rule   pollute   fuse   include

1 Jute is used for making mats, sacking, twine and rope.

2 The capsule is the nose cone of a rocket.

3 A flute is a woodwind instrument made from wood or metal.

4 Fumes from cars pollute the city.

5 Luke will salute the duke.

3 📖 Underline the **u–e** words. You should find 12.

Have you ever played on sand dunes? Do you know what a sand dune is? It is a small hill formed by strong winds whipping up fine sand. With a plastic tray or a flat-bottomed toboggan you can sit on top of a huge dune and then slide down to the bottom. Luke has the good fortune to live near the seaside and he often plays on sand dunes. He looks cute sitting on his tray flying down the slope to the water's edge. It is best to do this in sunny June when he can get up and run to the sea to jump and splash. He can amuse himself for ages. When Dad accuses him of not doing his homework he has no excuse.

4

Why did the fig go out with the prune?

He couldn't find a date.

69. The silent e rule

How do you add suffixes (endings) to words which end in silent **e**?

e.g.   like   +   ing   = ?

RULE

1

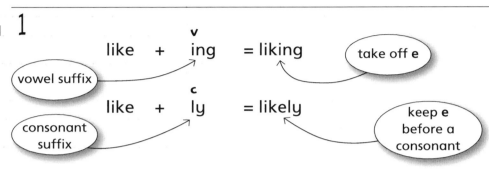

like   +   ing   = liking   take off **e**

vowel suffix

like   +   ly   = likely   keep **e** before a consonant

consonant suffix

2 Your turn. Complete this.

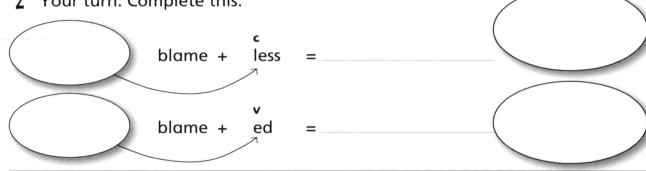

blame +   less   = _____

blame +   ed   = _____

3 Now do these word sums

1 *stripe* + *ed*   = _____

2 *brave* + *ly*   = _____

3 *use*   + *ing* = _____

4 *blame* + *less* = _____

5 *hire*   + *ed*   = _____

6 *state* + *ment* = _____

7 *smoke* + *y*   = _____

8 *home* + *less* = _____

9 *amuse* + *ment* = _____

10 *smile* + *ing* = _____

Essential spellings

Work across. ⟶

Read	Trace, naming letters	Write
1 change	*change*	
2 know	*know*	
3 leave	*leave*	
4 told	*told*	
5 write	*write*	
6 near	*near*	
7 during	*during*	
8 above	*above*	
9 below	*below*	
10 both	*both*	

71. Long-vowel pattern E–E e–e e-e

Colour the long-vowel pattern <u>red</u>.

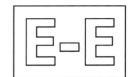

1 Say **athlete** 🔊. The sound is the same as alphabetical name **E**.

A sup<u>re</u>m<u>e</u> athl<u>ete</u>

2 Trace and copy this sentence in your exercise book. ✏️

Pete and Eve compete with Steve.

3 Underline words which contain the **e–e** pattern. You should find 15.

e.g. <u>eve</u> the <u>severe</u> keep some wreck theme Pete for land trapeze interfere foot athlete pot these herring nest of complete tea junk supreme whisk centipede ginger delete force charm intercede because invite serene complete

4 Use the words in the box to complete the story.

> eve Pete athlete interfere supreme
> compete persevere extremely serene
> complete stampede depleted genes

P_____ was a top a_____.

It was in his g_____ as his father had been a s_____

a_____ before him. P_____ loved the excitement of the s_____

at the start of an important race, and even after a long run he never felt

that his energy was d_____. Sometimes he felt he could go on

running forever. P_____ wanted to c_____ at the Olympic games in

June. He was very optimistic about his prospects of winning a gold medal,

but he knew he would have to p_____ to keep on top form in order

to be selected. He would have to push himself e_____ hard to

c_____ the necessary fitness programme. On the e_____ of a

race P_____ always stayed s_____ and would not

let anything i_____ with his plan for being on winning form.

5

1 At the end of a word, silent **e** makes the vowel sound long. Choose from the words with short- or long-vowel sounds to fill the gaps in these sentences.

Mother wore a huge pink _____ to go to the wedding.   hat   hate

Fay _____ her bike up the steep hill.   rode   rod

The vixen has a small playful _____ to look after.   cub   cube

Did you fly to San Francisco on a British _____?   plan   plane

Rabbits _____ across the cool green grass in the evening.   hop   hope

Hopefully the sun will _____ in the morning.   shine shin

Jack lost his football _____ after the game last Tuesday.   kit   kite

Eve wore _____ short cream silk dress for the party.   here   her

Tom placed the _____ of toothpaste on the shelf.   tub   tube

_____ has a _____ hamster called Petal.   Pete   pet

2 Listen for the long-vowel sound in each word and write the word in the appropriate column. Track 30.

A)) e a–e	E)) e e–e	I)) e i–e	O)) e o–e	U)) e u–e

73. Long-vowel pattern AI ai *ai*

Colour the long-vowel pattern <u>red</u>.

1 Say **tail** [A](((. The sound is the same as alphabetical name **A**.

Two t**ai**ls make a p**ai**r.

2 Trace, then copy twice in your exercise book. Tick the one you like the best.

The rain in Spain stays mainly in the plain.

3 Put a ring around **ai**. (You should find 7.)

Ailailmaildetailg Ailmentsailingreliefispalaid

4 Listen to the CD at track 31. (◎)

Write *a* or *ai* in the box, depending on whether you hear the short-vowel sound [a](((or the long-vowel sound [A](((in the word.

1	2	3	4	5	6	7	8

5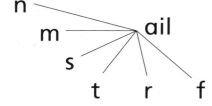

n		dr	
m — ail		br — ain	
s		st	
t r f		m r ag	

6 Choose two words from each group.
   Write the words in sentences of your own in your exercise book.

7

More about ai

1 📖 Highlight or underline **ai**.

I was waiting for a train in freezing weather on platform 4 at Kings Cross station, surrounded by a mountain of cases and bags of every shape and size. Suddenly I felt a sharp stabbing pain in my back. I felt faint and my legs went to jelly. I fell heavily amongst all the baggage and crashed to the floor. Coming round, I found myself in the waiting room. In next-to-no time a kind waiter came over with a cup of hot sweet tea and asked whether I needed help. Sipping the welcoming hot drink, I replied that I was feeling a little frail but did not want to miss my train. At that moment I heard that my train was delayed. Frost and ice had made the signals fail. I was angry at this delay, but full of praise for the kind waiter. I decided I would not complain to the rail company but I would consider going by car to the airport and then flying to my holiday in Scotland.

2

Across

5 Past tense of verb to pay. (4)
6 Walk up this to change floors. (9)
8 Keeps you out of jail for a time (4)
10 Mend. (6)
12 Use a hammer with it. (4)
13 It hurts. (4)
15 Small slow-moving animal with house. (5)
16 A mark on cloth. (5)
17 Middle of body. Measure your ____. (5)
19 Sit on it. (5)
20 Follow the nature ____ through the woods. (5)
21 Pleased with one's appearance. (4)
22 Letters. (4)

Down

1 Use it to think. (5)
2 First ____. Often needed after an accident. (3)
3 Bad weather: ____ stones. (4)
4 A bucket. (4)
5 Two of a kind, e.g. gloves. (4)
7 Trains run on this. (7)
8 Brilliant idea (using 1 down). (9)
9 Weak in body. (5)
11 Opposite of pass (in an exam). (4)
14 Grows on your head. (4)
16 On some boats. (4)
18 A happy dog wags it. (4)

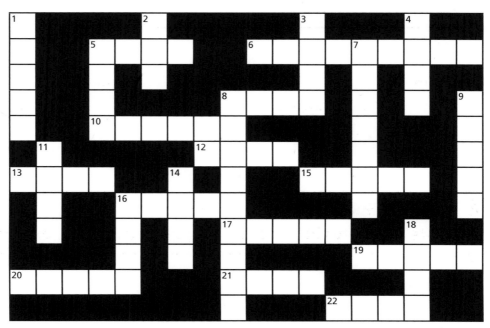

75. Working with letters and words you know

1

Read	Use your Reading/Spelling pack to make words	Name the letters	Write
sail			
leaf			
flute			
mole			
seat			
fail			
fuse			
slope			
some			
meal			

2 Write other words you have made in the boxes.

o-e	u-e	ea	ai

1 Say **cow** ow)).

How n**ow**, br**ow**n c**ow**.

2 Trace and copy this sentence in your exercise book.

A clown is not allowed to frown.

3 Put a ring around every **ow** pattern you can find.

e.g. howernswowvhowkoleosowzjorlrowmlakojowlflower
clowndforjthloaprrsdowntrowelgrowldjbnafkpnow

Did you find 12?

4 Write *ow* in the box if you hear ow)) in the word. Track 32.

1	2	3	4	5	6	7	8	9	10

5 clown   brown   crowd   powder   drowned   tower
drowsy   shower   growl   allow   down   flower   owl

Use these words to complete the sentences.

1 The _____ wore red _____ on his face and a _____ in his hat.

2 I will not _____ you to go to the top of the _____.

3 A _____ swooped _____ and made the _____
dog _____.

4 A sudden _____ of rain almost _____ the _____.

6 What do you call an eskimo's cow?   An eskimoo.

What's green and hairy and goes up and down?   A gooseberry in a lift.

R/S

77. Long-vowel pattern OW ow *ow*

Colour the long-vowel pattern red.

1 Say **snow** O))). The sound is the same as alphabetical name **O**.

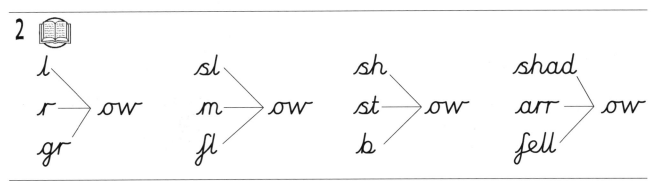

Sn**ow** makes the sn**ow**man gr**ow**.

2

l
r → ow
gr

sl
m → ow
fl

sh
st → ow
b

shad
arr → ow
fell

3

1 It's mine. I _____ it.

2 To plant seeds.

3 Opposite of fast.

4 Where the arm bends.

5 Made of glass. Part of a house.

6 Opposite of deep.

4 Use both words in each box to make sentences of your own.

1	crow/sparrow
2	slowly/flows
3	bow/arrow
4	pillow/yellow

5

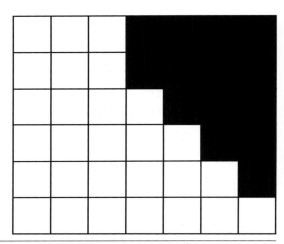

Where do snowmen dance?

At the snowball.

What happened to the kid who slept with his head under the pillow?

The fairies took all of his teeth away.

More about ow

.78

1 📖 Fill in the empty sound pictures.

The farmer sows seeds in the shallow furrows of the rich brown land beside

the gently flowing stream. He puts up a scarecrow to keep the sparrows

and crows away. He wants to grow rows of marrows on this narrow strip

of land that has been left fallow to allow it to become fertile again.

In the evening, followed by his dog, the old fellow slowly pushes his

wheelbarrow down the garden path and plants out seedlings with a

trowel. He will grow yellow flowers under the willow tree by the

window to make a bower.

Now read on.

The clock in the tower on the town hall strikes seven.
Rabbits skip around their burrows in the hollow. A light
glows through the window of the farmhouse and the farmer
begins to think about a bowl of hot food, a shower, a towel
and his dressing gown, but before that he must shut his fowls
up safely for the night. Tomorrow he must show his grown-
up son how to mow the meadow using the power mower which he has
borrowed.

Now it is bedtime and the farmer slowly lowers his head onto his pillow,
whilst outside the wind blows gently and the cows low in the barn.
A snowy owl screeches and a howling fox makes his dog growl.

2 🆂🅿 Copy these headings into your exercise book. Then listen to the
words your teacher says and write them in the appropriate column.

ow ᵒʷ)))	ow ᵒ)))

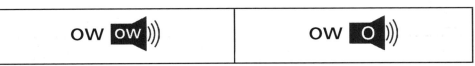

What did the
policeman say to
his tummy?

You're under
a vest.

79. Long-vowel pattern OA oa *oa*

Colour the long-vowel pattern red.

1 Say **goat** [O))]. The sound is the same
as alphabetical name **O**.

G<u>oa</u>ts afl<u>oa</u>t.

2 Trace and copy this sentence in your exercise book. (pencil icon)

The coach approached the coast road.

3 Word search

Find all the **oa** words. Underline them and then
write them out in joined-up writing in the space below.

hope	boat	mouse	toast	gown	blown	coat	throat	house
foal	round	float	note	moan	shroud	shoal	groan	down
slow	coal	out	broke	boast	snow	hound	own	poach	pouch

Now read these words aloud.

4 Listen to these words and write *ea* [E))] *ai* [A))] or *oa* [O))] in
the box according to the sound you hear in the word. Track 33. (CD icon)

1	2	3	4	5	6	7	8

More about oa

1 Link the rhyming pairs.
Use them to complete the rhymes below.

goats	boat	oats	coal
load	boast	cloak	coast
foal	croak	afloat	road

1 The old man kept a herd of _____ and fed them mainly on _____.
2 They put to sea in a _____ and hoped they would stay _____.
3 The lorry shed its _____ right in the middle of the _____.
4 The Captain began to _____ that at last he could see the _____.
5 The mare was proud of her _____ which, like her, was as black as _____.
6 The frog with the terrible _____ changed into a prince with a _____.

2

Across

2 Will the boat ____?
5 Get up and ____
6 Where the land meets the sea:____
7 As black as ____
8 Put to sea in a ____
10 Look ____ me
11 Almost like a weasel:____
12 I told him____
13 He had a sore ____
15 To trap and steal wild animals:____

Down

1 A tree which grows from an acorn: ____
2 Baby horse: ____
3 To make a promise, he swore an ____
4 Like a large frog: ____
5 Sheep-like animal which eats anything: ____
6 Put this on to keep warm when you go out: ____
7 A kind of bus: ____
9 Ground ____ meal makes porridge
11 Use to wash yourself or your clothes: ____
12 I told you ____
14 Let's go ____ the party

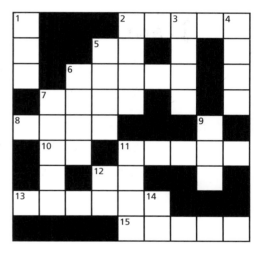

3

The fancy dress party was held at the old coach house. The fellow with the bow and arrow and green coat was Robin Hood. Snow White wore a flowing yellow gown and a velvet cloak. Old King Cole boasted a golden crown. Coco the clown was in the cloakroom fixing a flower on his hat. The Fairy Godmother floated by with a sparkling necklace at her throat.

4

Why doesn't Cinderella play football well?

Because she has a pumpkin for a coach.

Permission to Photocopy

81. Long-vowel pattern -IGH -igh -igh

Colour the long-vowel pattern red.

1 Say **night** 🔊. The sound is the
same as alphabetical name **I**.

A bad fr**igh**t on a dark n**igh**t!

2 Trace and copy this sentence in your exercise book. ✏️

We need a brighter light tonight.

3 Underline **-igh** and 📖.

e.g.   n**igh**t   light   right   sight   fright   bright
frightening   high   slightly   sigh   thighs   fighting

4 Complete the sentences using words from Section 3.

1 We must try day and _____ to get it _____.

2 The _____ of his ugly face gave her a _____.

3 The cave was dark and the _____ from his torch was
not very _____.

4 "Must you children always be _____?" asked their
mother with a _____.

5 The floodwater rose until it was as _____ as
his _____.

6 A wild animal might find being stroked _____
very _____.

1

One day last summer, Ben and Neesha decided to
go onto the moors to try out Ben's new kite. He
liked to enter the kite-flying contest every year.
He always made his kites himself and it was vital
to try out this new model and get some practice at
flying it before the big event in a fortnight's time.
The wind was quite strong and the kite flapped
and fluttered higher and higher until it was just
a bright red and white square in the sky. Neesha
was very excited and the look of delight on Ben's
face was a happy sight. "Let me try!" begged
Neesha, so Ben reluctantly started to hand her the string. Suddenly Neesha
stepped backwards into a slight hole, lost her balance and fell over, letting
out a loud scream. At the same moment, a strong gust of wind tore the
string from her hand. Ben was just in time to leap up and grasp the end
as it whisked past his ear. Luckily there was no harm done to Ben's kite or
Neesha's spine and they are still friends.

2 Listen to the CD and write the word in the correct column. Track 34. ◎

i-e	-igh	-y

3

Why did the
teacher wear
dark glasses?

Her class
was too bright.

What did the
big candle say to
the little candle?

I'm going out
tonight.

Beat the clock word race

shave	might	why	clothes	leave

coat	whole	square	white	pray

place	write	town	tune	tore

judge	change	garden	balloon	happy

inside	below	paper	important	between

started	morning	orbit	replying	seventy

family	stories	admire	compare	crayon

fancy	cycling	pencil	understood	gentle

floating	following	crowning	frightening	dreamer

Time yourself.
Can you beat your time?

1 .... minutes .... seconds

2 .... minutes .... seconds

How much have you learned?

1 Write the word for each picture in joined-up handwriting.

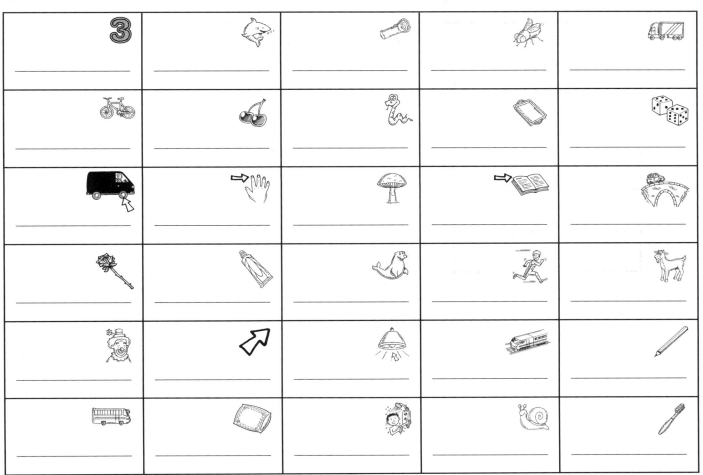

2 📖 , then follow track 35. 💿 ✏️

  1 Can you say the name of the train?

  2 Take that snail away from here.

  3 They chose their boat at the show.

  4 The roads were closed because of the snow.

  5 Pete drinks green tea.

  6 It is easy to get rid of these weeds.

  7 Spike likes to fly high in the sky.

  8 Why don't you try to write a letter to your gran tonight?

  9 Use a tool to mend the fuse.

  10 The students said the rules were confusing.

3 (Sp) Ask your teacher for a spelling test.

Certificate of Merit

Presented to

_____

for the successful completion of

Beat Dyslexia! Book 4

Signed _____ (Teacher)

Date _____

A	B	C	D
E	F	G	H
I	J	K	L
M	N	O	P

Q	R	S	T
U	V	W	X
Y	Z	birthday	eyes
children	work	money	around

sure	heard	suddenly	during
thought	different	know	following
world	right	together	through
young	great	earth	important

a b c d
e f g h i
j k l m n
o p q r
s t u v
w x y z

Practice sheet for handwriting